Shopkins™

Once you shop...You can't stop!

ANNUAL 2017

This SHOPKINS™ book belongs to:

Lily Murdoch

centum

WHAT'S INSIDE?

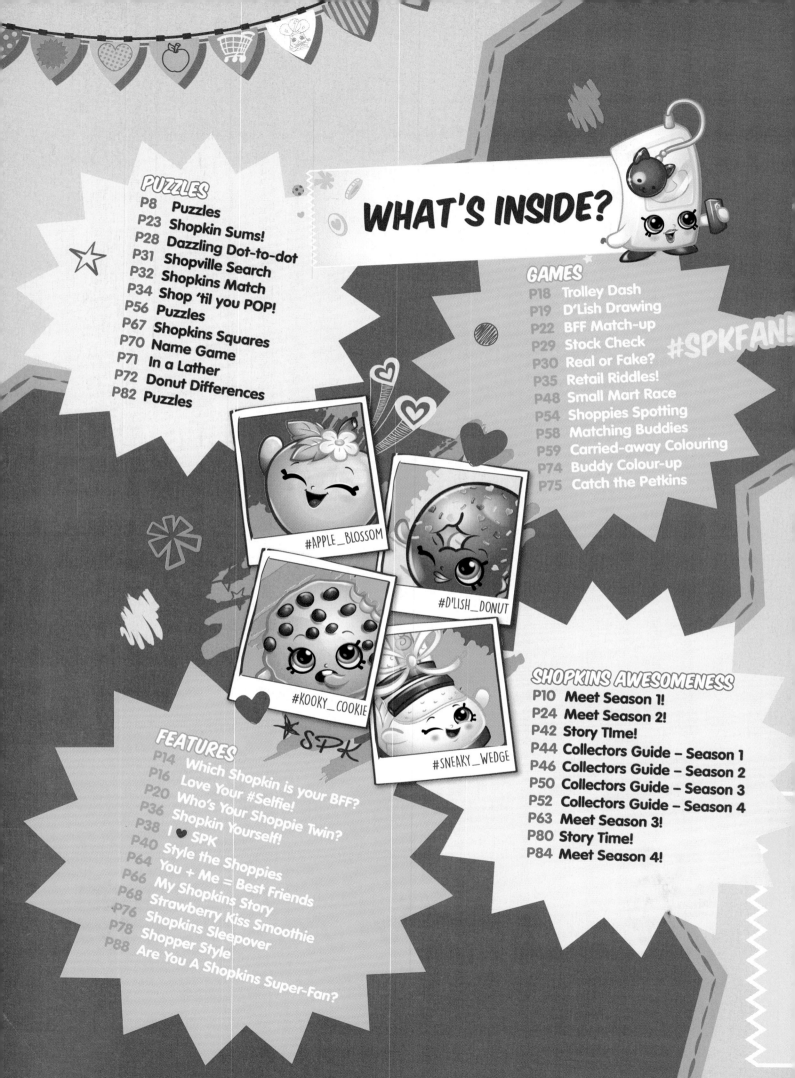

#SPKFAN!

#APPLE_BLOSSOM

#D'LISH_DONUT

#KOOKY_COOKIE

*SPK

#SNEAKY_WEDGE

WELCOME TO SHOPVILLE!

Shopkins collectors, get ready for VIP access to an adorable adventure! All your favourite characters from across the Seasons are waiting for you, from Apple Blossom to Kooky Cookie, Poppy Corn to Cupcake Chic, Taco Terrie to Sneaky Sally … and loads more. (Miss Pressy asked for a special mention!)

And all the Shoppies are here too! Jessicake, Popette, Bubbleisha, Donatina and the totally gorgeous, minty-haired Peppa-Mint have loads of styling and friendship games, just for you.

Finally, don't forget the super-cute and totally awesome Petkins, who definitely want to play!

ONCE YOU SHOP... YOU CAN'T STOP

LOOK FOR THE LIMITED EDITION SHOPKINS!

Can you find these oh-so-special Season 4 Shopkins hiding in this book? Each one appears in a yellow star. Tick them off here as you find them!

 Pretty Puff ☐   Frenchy Perfume ☐   Gemma Bottle ☐

 Pretty Bow Kay ☐   Sparkly Spritz ☐   Sally Scent ☐

BLIND BAG

Which fruity friends are hiding inside these shoppers?
Write their names before they pop right out!

1. _ _ _ _ _ _ _

2. _ _ _ _ _ _ _ _

3. _ _ _ _ _ _

4. _ _ _ _ _ _ _ _

5. _ _ _ _ _

6. _ _ _ _ _ _ _ _

MYSTERY SHOPKIN

Ooh, who is it? Cross out all of the letter pairs, then unscramble the remaining letters to reveal a citrus-bright Shopkin from Season 2.

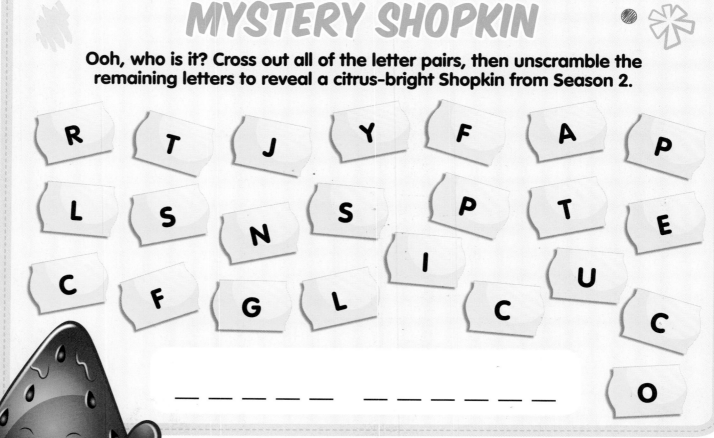

R T J Y F A P

L S N S P T E

C F G L I C U

C

O

_ _ _ _ _ _   _ _ _ _ _ _

ANSWERS ON
PAGE 92

SHOPKIN SHADOWS

Can you work out who these cute shadows belong to?

① ② ③

sneaky wedge

④ ⑤ ⑥

I'll tell you a secret – they're all from Season 3, like me!

AISLE BE QUICK!

Hurry, it's nearly closing time and the Shopkins need to get back to their own aisles. Which route should each character take?

FRUIT & VEG   DAIRY   HEALTH & BEAUTY

MEET SEASON 1

DAIRY

CHEE ZEE
A confident performer who loves taking centre stage – and is a little bit crackers!
♥s rapping with his BFFs.

GOOGY
Clumsy and shy, his friends try to get him to come out of his shell.
♥s juggling!

SPILT MILK
A bit of a klutz and a born risk-taker, she likes to stir things up.
♥s skimming through comic books.

SWISS MISS
A hilarious jokester and stand-up comedian.
♥s cheesy jokes!

BAKERY

KOOKY COOKIE
Really shy and sensitive, her friends encourage her to try new things.
♥s thinking outside the cookie jar.

D'LISH DONUT
Super sweet but with a competitive edge.
♥s trying for the perfect hole-in-one.

MINI MUFFIN
Sweet inside and out, with a lot of energy.
♥s mornings – she's an early riser!

BREAD HEAD
Independent and confident and a bit of a chatterbox.
♥s chatting on the phone!

APPLE BLOSSOM
An adventurer with big dreams and kind to the core.
♥s going on adventures!

STRAWBERRY KISS
A daydreamer with a huge imagination and often away with the fairies!
♥s writing poetry.

MELONIE PIPS
Refreshing to be around. Likes to get involved and always loves a slice of the action!
♥s dancing to 'Pip-Hop' music!

POSH PEAR
She's a bit spoilt, but is a good listener and friendly.
♥s playing cards.

FRUIT & VEG

PINEAPPLE CRUSH
Silly and fun and a lover of the sun!
♥s surfing and sunbaking.

MISS MUSHY MOO
A bit of a softy but with a good head on her shoulders.
♥s making mud pies!

SODA POPS
Super bubbly and sweet, she adds fizz to any party.

♥ s shaking it on the dance floor!

WOBBLES
A bit klutzy and a worry wart, but she loves to jiggle on the dance floor.

♥ s hip hop dancing!

RAINBOW BITE
Optimistic and adventurous, she always looks on the positive side of life.

♥ s painting!

WISHES
A real party starter and a bit of an attention seeker.

♥ s singing for anyone who'll listen!

FAIRY CRUMBS
Cute and colourful with a love for all things pink and purple.

♥ s parties!

PRETZ-ELLE
A little scatter-brained, but also cheeky and charming.

♥ s gymnastics!

CHEEZEY B
A Shopkin who never stops rhyming.

♥ s rapping with his BFFs!

PANTRY

PEPPE PEPPER
Always sneezing! He's clever and kind and a bit of a daredevil.

♥ s spicing things up!

SALLY SHAKES
She adds some fun and flavour to any party.

♥ s rock climbing!

SUGAR LUMP
A real sweety who gets along with everyone.

♥ s perfecting the ultimate cup of tea!

BREAKY CRUNCH
Full of energy and ready to go at a moment's notice.

♥ s working out!

GRAN JAM
Caring, gentle and the mother of the group.

♥ s knitting and jamming on the ukulele!

TOMMY KETCHUP
Extremely cheeky and always wants to be a part of everything.

♥ s trolley riding!

MEET SEASON 1

LIPPY LIPS
A fashionista with sassy style, and maybe a bit bossy!
❤s shopping, of course!

SHAMPY
We never know if she's Silky or Shampy!
❤s smelling fresh!

SILKY
Partners-in-crime with Shampy, with a great sense of style!
❤s swimming!

SCRUBS
Chatty and always grinning, she loves to make people smile.
❤s tubing!

POLLY POLISH
A fashion risk-taker who's always trying new colours.
❤s telling the unvarnished truth!

FROZEN

COOL CUBE
A bit of a snow bunny, who hates hot weather.
❤s snowboarding and sledging!

ICE CREAM DREAM
Scoops of fun but maybe a bit of a headache at times.
❤s building igloos!

SNOW CRUSH
A snowkin builder extraordinaire.
❤s snowkin building and curling.

POPSI COOL
Cold on the outside but warm and gooey on the inside!
❤s ice skating.

YO-CHI
Well cultured and different each day.
❤s swirling around the dance floor!

FREEZY PEAZY
Super cool and the best rapper in the pod.
❤s rapping with his BFFs!

CHEEKY CHOCOLATE
Always laughing, having fun and never afraid to get dirty.
❤s playing pranks!

LOLLI POPPINS
As sweet as can be! She loves smiling and making Shopkins laugh.
❤s hairdressing!

BUBBLES
She can talk a LOT, but is really kind and caring.
❤s singing a tune!

LE'QUORICE
She's old fashioned but still the life of any party.
❤s playing hopscotch!

SWEET TREATS

CANDY KISSES
Romantic and smooth, although he hasn't had a date just yet.
❤s swriting poetry!

JELLY B
Full of beans with a colourful personality.
❤s skipping!

CUPCAKE QUEEN

Super sweet and a
keeper of the peace.

♥ s hosting grand balls!

BUTTERCUP

Mellow and yellow but cute
enough to melt any hearts.

♥ s his great taste!

TIN'A'TUNA

He often thinks there's something fishy
going on and loves canned applause.

♥ s swimming upstream.

TWINKY WINKS

She says Shopkins are the
cream of the crop but can
sponge off her friends a bit.

♥ s surprising her friends!

PAPA TOMATO

A story teller who adds flavour
to everything he does.

♥ s chatting with pals on the vine.

SUNNY SCREEN

Over protective and a bit
of a worry wart.

♥ s nice weather – the hotter,
the better!

EXCLUSIVES

SPONGECAKE

A Shopkin who loves to party! She takes
the cake when it comes to being the most
colorful character in the room!

♥ s playing party games.

LA' LOTION

A beautiful looking Shopkin who
really takes care of herself... She's
always giving out beauty advice.

♥ s reading gossip magazines.

COCO NUTTY

A little kooky and a lot nutty, but
very easy going and relaxed. Always
dreaming about lying under a palm tree!

♥ s sunbaking.

MARGARINA

Super helpful! A real softy who
likes to spread herself around
and help where she can.

♥ s buttering up her friends.

ROLLY ROLL

A Shopkin who loves food and
will never let you down.
Always by your side if there's a
plate of food around!

♥ s roller skating.

PUMPKINELLA

She may not look it but she's no
ordinary pumpkin. Pumpkinella
loves going to Royal Balls, but is
never out after midnight!

♥ s going on carriage rides.

HOT APPLE PIE

Warm on the inside and
sweet on the outside.
Sometimes she's too hot
to handle!

♥ s baking for her friends.

CURLY FRIES

A quite and shy little fry.
Would much rather curl up with a
good book than go out and play!

♥ s watching
Shirley Temple
Movies.

WHICH SHOPKIN IS YOUR BFF?

How adorable are the Season 4 characters? Which one would you be hanging out in the aisles with? Try this fun quiz to find out.

YOUR BFF IS

PETA PLANT!

YOUR BFF IS

ICE CREAM QUEEN!

YOUR BFF IS

MISS PRESSY!

START HERE
Is your fave Shopkin a Petkin?

 NO

Do you like trying new hairstyles?

YES

Is spring better than autumn?

YES

Is your favourite flower pink?

 NO

YES

Are savoury snacks better than sweet?

NO

YES

Do you love surprises?

YES

Are pink and purple just the BEST?

 NO

YES

Can you ever eat too much ice cream?

YES

NO

Your birthday – best day of the year?

YES → Have you ever peeked at a gift before you should?

NO ↓

YES ↗

Are pop stars better than movie stars?

NO → Could you spend hours at the shops?

YES →

YES ↓ (Have you ever peeked at a gift before you should?) **NO** ↓

YES ↑

Do you do Shopkin swaps with your friends?

YES ↑

NO ↓

YES →

Could you spend hours at the shops?

Are you the loudest of your friends?

NO →

YES ↗

NO ↑

Are puppies the cutest pets?

NO → Do you totally love to dance?

LOVE YOUR #SELFIE!

Check out Smarty Phone's top tips for super-cute selfies.

BESTIES FOR LIFE!

LIGHT IT UP

Natural light from a window or outdoors is best. Make sure the sun is in front of you to avoid shadows.

FRAME IT

Pause before you click to check out what's in the picture. Move your camera around for the best shot, and lift it up high to fit more in. You can crop it after, too.

LET'S GET IT POPPIN'

YEAH!

GO PROP-TASTIC!

You can buy fun prop kits or, even better, make your own. Challenge your buddies to come up with a prop that says something about them, then snap away!

WHAT'S NOT TO LOVE!?

SPK xOx

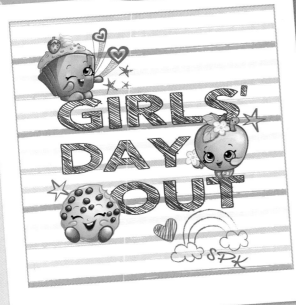

GIRLS' DAY OUT

SPK

STICK WITH IT!

If you want to fit in more BFFs or a cool background, you'll need a selfie stick. It has a clamp to hold your camera or phone and an extendable arm with a button on the end. Just lift and click!

BE SUPER SILLY

Smiley pics are nice, but funny pics are SO awesome! Who can take the most fabulously funny selfie?

FUN WITH FILTERS

Add cool effects at the touch of a button! There are lots of free apps that can spice up your snaps.

ANSWERS ON
PAGE 92

TROLLEY DASH

It's a busy day in Shopsville! Grab your favourite Shopkins by
drawing lines to put them into the correct baskets.

WHICH SHOPKIN
BELONGS IN
ANOTHER AISLE?
CIRCLE HER.

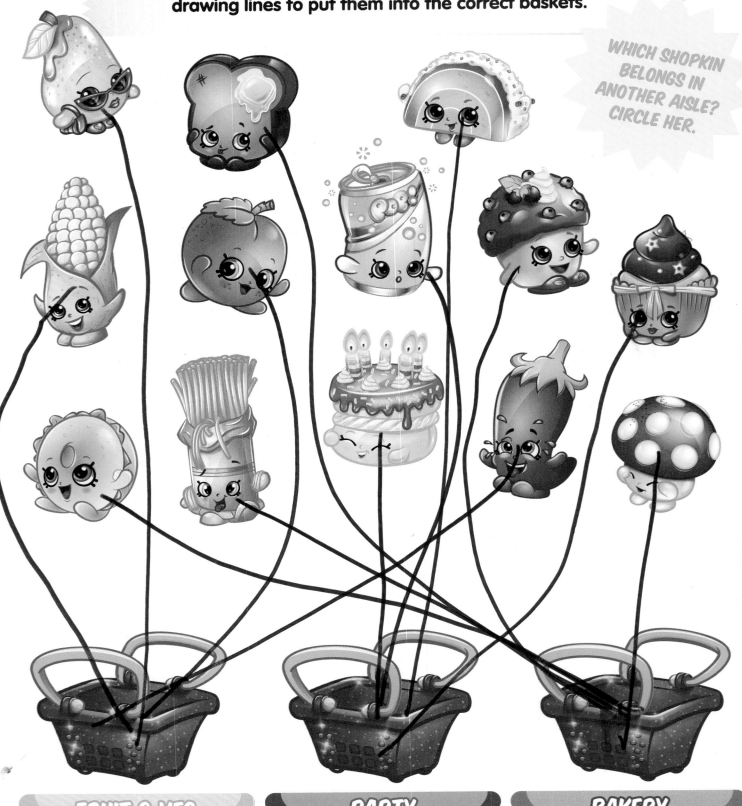

FRUIT & VEG   PARTY   BAKERY

D'LISH DRAWING

This GLAZED SWEETIE is iced to perfection! Copy D'Lish Donut into the grid below square by square.

Now sprinkle her with COLOUR.

WHO'S YOUR SHOPPIE TWIN?

WHICH SUPER-CUTE SHOPPIE ARE YOU MOST LIKE? TICK THE WORDS AND PHRASES THAT ARE SO YOU.

- ☐ I bubble gum.
- ☐ Everything should be pink.
- ☐ Okay, I get moody.
- ☐ Friends should share secrets.
- ☐ Plaits are super-cute.

- ☐ Popcorn is totally yum.
- ☐ It's true ... I'm loud.
- ☐ Every moment needs a selfie.
- ☐ Movies are my life.
- ☐ I can't stop talking.

- ☐ Always smiling.
- ☐ I could shop forever.
- ☐ I love to treat my pets.
- ☐ Cupcakes = awesome.
- ☐ Fashion bows are cute.

- ☐ Daydream all day.
- ☐ Donuts = amazing.
- ☐ Sweet to friends? Always.
- ☐ I'm always the agony aunt.
- ☐ Fun comes first.

- ☐ A BIT of a drama queen.
- ☐ Super-shy? That's me.
- ☐ My BFFs are awesome.
- ☐ I always get the goss.
- ☐ Ice cream is the BEST.

COUNT UP YOUR ANSWERS IN EACH COLOUR TO FIND OUT YOUR SHOPPIE MATCH!

Blue ☐   Yellow ☐   Pink ☐   Green ☐   Purple ☐

MOSTLY BLUE
Your Shoppie twin is ...
JESSICAKE
You're a cupcake cutie and a real sweetie. Smart and sensible, you love to treat your friends to cute handmade gifts.

MOSTLY YELLOW
Your Shoppie twin is ...
POPETTE
You're a bowl lot of fun! Loud and loveable, your favourite thing to do is to chill out with friends and a good movie.

MOSTLY GREEN
Your Shoppie twin is ...
PEPPA-MINT
You may sometimes lose your cool, but that's because you're so warm-hearted. And you always have the scoop on the gossip!

MOSTLY PINK
Your Shoppie twin is ...
BUBBLEISHA
You're bubble trouble! You're strong-willed and full of opinions, but your besties know just how sweet you can be.

MOSTLY PURPLE
Your Shoppie twin is ...
DONATINA
You're happy-dough-lucky! You may be a bit of a daydreamer, but when your friends need you, you're always around.

BFF MATCH-UP

The Shopkins are all friends – but like Shampy and Silky, some Shopkins are just destined to be BFFs! Can you work out where the missing characters fit in this friendship chart?

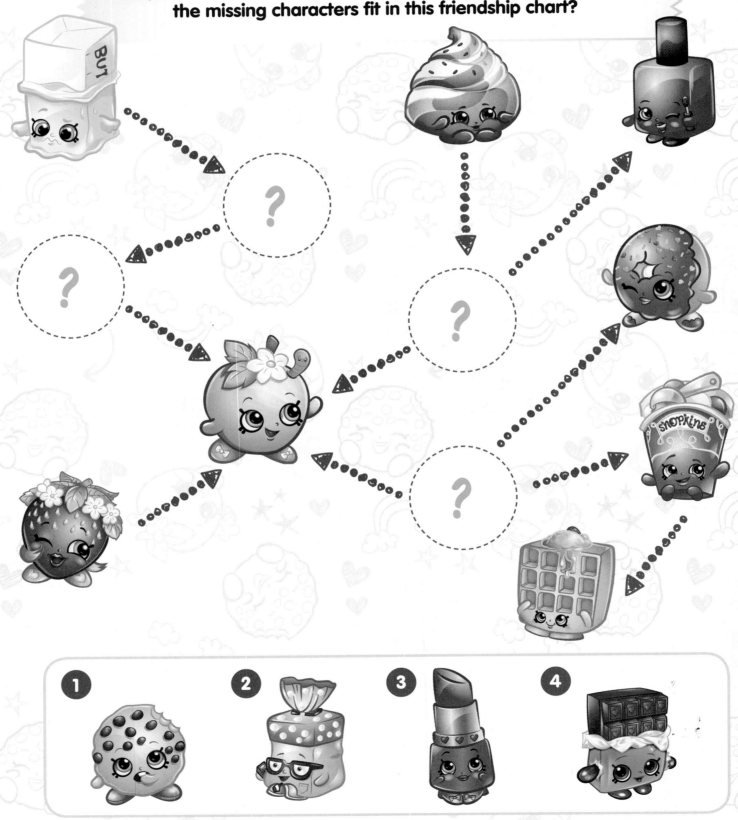

ANSWERS ON PAGE 92

SHOPKIN SUMS!

Is this the best trolley-load EVER? It's overflowing with Shopkins! How many can you count in total?

There are ☐☐ Shopkins.

Can you spot **GRAN JAM'S** sweet smile?

23

MEET SEASON 2

JUICY ORANGE
Maybe a little pushy, she can put the squeeze on you.

♥ s keeping juicy secrets!

CORNY COB
His friends think he's a bit corny – but you'd have to 'husk' them about that!

♥ s doing puzzles and maizes.

DIPPY AVOCADO
A true greenie who likes to spread himself around.

♥ s taking a dip on a hot day.

CHLOE FLOWER
A bit of a hippy and all about "flower power". Never 'leafs' her friends behind.

♥ s leafing through the newspaper.

SILLY CHILLI
Some friends think he comes across as cold, but he's really just a little chilli!

♥ s eating very HOT dogs.

SNEAKY WEDGE
Footloose and fancy-free, but gets a little tongue-tied now and then.

♥ s hanging out in the gym.

BETTY BOOT
Gets her kicks riding high in the saddle, she's the wildest boot in the West.

♥ s boot scootin'!

BUN BUN SLIPPER
A bit of a snoozy head who is always ready for bed. She'd better hop to it!

♥ s doing the bunny hop dance.

SHOES

PROMMY
High-spirited and never flat, she is known for her fabulous style.

♥ s kicking up her heels!

HEELS
Always a hard worker, she buckles down and gets on with things.

♥ s tap dancing!

POPPY CORN

She knows how to bag a bargain and can shop 'til she pops!

♥ s going to the movies.

ICE-CREAM DREAM

A little bit drippy but never loses her cool. She's cool, cone and collected!

♥ s chilling out in her own cone.

WAFFLE SUE

A total chatterbox who loves to stay toasty warm!

♥ s waffling on about anything.

PAMELA PANCAKE

Stacks of fun! Overflowing with sweetness, but never too syrupy.

♥ s flipping out in the diving pool.

MINNIE MINTIE

A breath of fresh air! She's cool to be around, with hugs and kisses for everyone.

♥ s yoga and deep breathing.

TOASTY POP

He never has a stale idea and always pops up with new stuff.

♥ s throwing parties and giving toasts!

LANA LAMP

Loves light-hearted jokes and coming up with bright ideas.

♥ s reading in bed.

BRENDA BLENDER

A smooth operator who sometimes stirs up trouble.

♥ s mixing with her friends.

HOMEWARES

ZAPPY MICROWAVE

A real fast thinker who wants everything done yesterday!

♥ s speed-reading.

SIZZLES

Warm-hearted rather than hot-tempered, she loves to steam through her jobs!

♥ s riding on steam trains.

MEET SEASON 2

CUPCAKE CHIC

A fun-filled girl whose cup is always overflowing with sweet thoughts!

♥ s baking up new ideas to treat her friends!

PECANNA PIE

A bit nutty in the head but a real sweetheart inside!

♥ s going to the ballet, especially 'The Nutcracker'.

MARY MERINGUE

Sweet and fluffy, she always has her head in the clouds.

♥ s whipping up treats!

CARRIE CARROT CAKE

Sweet but a little nutty. People say she has a 24-carrot heart of gold!

♥ s horse riding!

SLICK BREADSTICK

Crusty on the outside, but warm on the inside!

♥ s lunching in a French café.

FIFI FRUIT TART

A bit of a fruit loop, who likes to mix things up!

♥ s catching some sun so she's just ripe.

DUM MEE MEE

A peacekeeper who is no dummy when it comes to stopping tears.

♥ s rocking out with babies.

BABY PUFF

A sweet-smelling Shopkin who never makes rash decisions!

♥ s finding shapes in the clouds.

NAPPY DEE

A hard worker in any weather, wet or dry, night or day! It's a big job for a little nappy!

♥ s dancing her pants off!

BABY

DRIBBLES

When she hears a cry for help, this little squirt can save the day!

♥ s taking nice warm baths.

SIPPY SIPS

Never spills a secret and likes to be held tight.

♥ s singing lullabies.

BABY SWIPES

A real clean machine, she keeps things shiny from top to bottom.

♥ s swiping out in a wave.

PANTRY

CORNELL MUSTARD
A little squirt with big flavour who can make any hot dog a little hotter.

♥s solving mysteries.

AL FOIL
Strong and protective, but he can get torn between friends.

♥s wrapping with his friends.

FASTA PASTA
A great friend to twirl around with, and totally unspaghettable!

♥s shooting hoops with meatballs.

FI FI FLOUR
A little bit messy to be around, but she'll help anybody in a sticky situation.

♥s half-baked ideas!

HONEEEY
She can bee charming, she can bee helpful, and she loves to bee sweet!

♥s the spelling bee and catching flies.

CLEANING & LAUNDRY

MOLLY MOPS
Buckets of fun! She's a real hard worker with a shiny personality.

♥s playing mopscotch.

SQUEAKY CLEAN
Honest and clean-cut, she's in a 'glass' of her own!

♥s writing poetry.

SWEEPS
Don't just brush past Sweeps, she'll be your friend from dust 'til dawn!

♥s brushing up on her schooling.

WENDY WASHER
A truthful Shopkin who lays it on the line. She's a clean-living girl!

♥s spin cycle classes at the gym.

LEAFY
A girl who knows her roll in life, she always feels flushed with success!

♥s unwinding with a good magazine.

MARSHA MELLOW
A real softie who doesn't like the heat!

♥s camping out around the fire.

RUB-A-GLOVE
The Queen of Clean when it comes to dishing up sparkling plates.

♥s water sports.

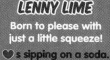

LENNY LIME
Born to please with just a little squeeze!

♥s sipping on a soda.

LIMITED EDITION

LEE TEA
She gets stronger with time and loves a dip in a hot tub.

♥s handbags, shoulder bags and tea bags.

DONNA DONUT
Every day is a great day with Donna, but the best are Fry-Days.

♥s a hole lot of stuff!

ANGIE ANKLE BOOT
Known for taking problems in her stride, and never too big for her boots.

♥s disco dancing.

DAZZLING DOT-TO-DOT

Which beautiful Shopkin loves to leave her mark wherever she goes? Join the dots to find out.

Delight this fashionista with a gloss of **HOT PINK** when you finish.

SPK
xOx

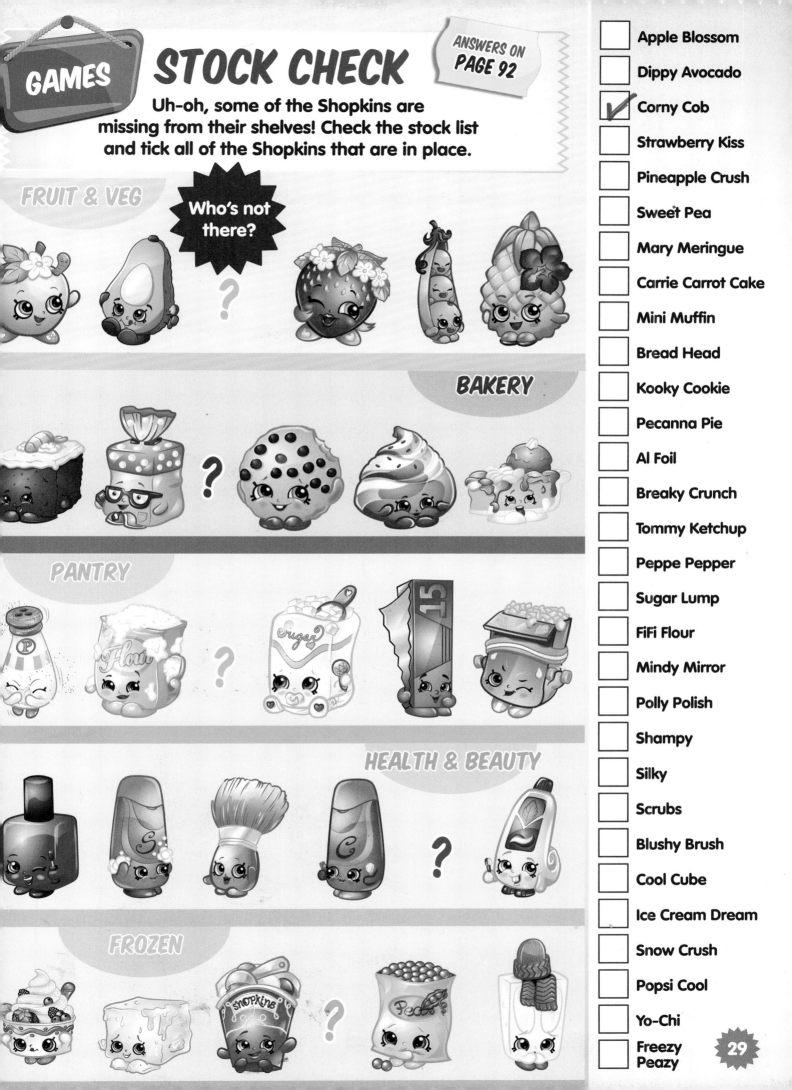

STOCK CHECK

ANSWERS ON
PAGE 92

Uh-oh, some of the Shopkins are
missing from their shelves! Check the stock list
and tick all of the Shopkins that are in place.

FRUIT & VEG

Who's not
there?

?

BAKERY

?

PANTRY

?

15

HEALTH & BEAUTY

?

FROZEN

SHOPKINS

?

Peas

- [ ] Apple Blossom
- [ ] Dippy Avocado
- [x] Corny Cob
- [ ] Strawberry Kiss
- [ ] Pineapple Crush
- [ ] Sweet Pea
- [ ] Mary Meringue
- [ ] Carrie Carrot Cake
- [ ] Mini Muffin
- [ ] Bread Head
- [ ] Kooky Cookie
- [ ] Pecanna Pie
- [ ] Al Foil
- [ ] Breaky Crunch
- [ ] Tommy Ketchup
- [ ] Peppe Pepper
- [ ] Sugar Lump
- [ ] FiFi Flour
- [ ] Mindy Mirror
- [ ] Polly Polish
- [ ] Shampy
- [ ] Silky
- [ ] Scrubs
- [ ] Blushy Brush
- [ ] Cool Cube
- [ ] Ice Cream Dream
- [ ] Snow Crush
- [ ] Popsi Cool
- [ ] Yo-Chi
- [ ] Freezy Peazy

29

REAL OR FAKE?

Are these facts about the Shopkins true or made up?
Add ticks to the ones you think are real, and crosses to
the ones you think are sooo fake.

Cool Cube loves winter sports.

✓ **1**

Waffle Sue is super quiet.

☐ **2**

3 **Corny Cob loves doing puzzles and maizes.** ☐

Poppy Corn has never been to the movies. **4**

✗

Sneaky Wedge's favourite game is 'Hide and Sneak'. ☐ **5**

Zappy Microwave is an excellent speed reader. ✓ **6**

Penny Pencil's BFF is Candy Apple. **7** ☐

Cornell Mustard can be a little chilly. **8** ☐

SHOPVILLE SEARCH

Can you find all of the super Shopkins words
in the wordsearch?

ANSWERS ON PAGE 92

J	A	T	R	O	L	L	E	Y	B
I	S	Z	A	L	F	O	I	L	A
U	I	S	V	I	M	P	L	G
T	P	A	N	T	R	Y	E	C
S	T	O	C	K	V	V	A	H
B	A	K	E	R	Y	Q	Q	F	A
R	A	I	B	N	K	Z	Q	Y	T
M	A	C	C	A	R	O	O	N	T
C	H	E	C	K	O	U	T	Y	E
D	A	I	R	Y	U	W	V	Q	R

TROLLEY   TILL   DAIRY
BAG   STOCK   PANTRY
CHECKOUT   BAKERY

1
_ _ _ _ _ _ _ _

Write the
names of these
cute Season 2
characters.

2
_ _ _ _ _ _ _

3
_ _ _ _ _ _ _ _ _

Can you find
us in the
grid, too?

4
_ _ _ _ _

SHOPKINS MATCH

EACH SHOPPIE HAS HER OWN ADORABLE SHOPKIN BESTIES. CAN YOU DRAW LINES TO MATCH THE SHOPPIES TO THEIR TWO SHOPKINS?

ANSWERS ON PAGE 92

GIRLS' DAY OUT

ALL OF THE SHOPPIES ARE READY FOR A FUN DAY AT THE SHOPS! CAN YOU FIT THEIR NAMES AND THE SHOPPIE WORDS INTO THE GRID?

JESSICAKE
POPETTE
DONATINA
BUBBLEISHA
PEPPAMINT
SHOP
BESTIES
DREAM

PHOTOBOMB!

WHICH SILLY SHOPKINS HAVE SNEAKED INTO THE SHOPPIES' SELFIE? WRITE THEIR NAMES HERE!

1 Lolly popins
2 _____ ____
3 heels
4 _____ _____
5 _____ _____

SHOP 'TIL YOU POP!

Poppy Corn and her pals are bags of fun! Can you spot 6 differences between the pictures?

#SPKSELFIE xox

SPKSELFIE xox

Colour a little Pop Star for every difference you find.

RETAIL RIDDLES!

ANSWERS ON PAGE 92

Can you guess who these riddles are about? Match each riddle to a Shopkin on this page.

HONEEEY

PRETZ-ELLE

1 This Shopkin is a giver not a taker.

2 This jiggly Shopkin goes perfectly with ice cream.

3 You might smell this pretty Shopkin before you see her.

BUN BUN SLIPPER

4 This cute baked good is all in a twist.

5 A super-cute Shopkin for toasty-warm toes.

JUNE BALLOON

6 This sweet 'n' sticky girl couldn't bee more happy.

WOBBLES

SPARKLY SPRITZ

7 This little party Shopkin is full of hot air!

MISS PRESSY

SHOPKIN YOURSELF!

Wouldn't you just LOVE to create your own Shopkin?
Try it now with this super-fun game.

WHAT WOULD BE YOUR SHOP HANGOUT?

PANTRY	SHOES	CLEANING & LAUNDRY	HOMEWARES
GO TO A	GO TO B	GO TO C	GO TO D

A WHICH COLOUR IS CUTEST?

| GO TO 1 | GO TO 2 | GO TO 3 | GO TO 4 |

B CHOOSE THE COOLEST SYMBOL.

| GO TO 5 | GO TO 6 | GO TO 7 | GO TO 8 |

C WHICH CHARACTER MAKES YOU MELT?

| GO TO 9 | GO TO 10 | GO TO 11 | GO TO 12 |

D WHICH SHOPPING CARRIER IS BEST?

| GO TO 13 | GO TO 14 | GO TO 15 | GO TO 16 |

USE YOUR IMAGINATION AND FILL IN THE FIRST NAME OF YOUR VERY OWN TEENY-TINY SHOPKIN!

1 _____ Sauce

2 _____ Biscuit

3 _____ Herb

4 _____ Sugar

5 _____ Sandal

6 _____ Trainer

7 _____ Laces

8 _____ Pump

9 _____ Squeegee

10 _____ Duster

11 _____ Scrubby

12 _____ Sponge

13 _____ Heater

14 _____ Desk

15 _____ Juicer

16 _____ Dryer

NOW DRAW WHAT YOUR ADORABLE SHOPKIN CHARACTER LOOKS LIKE!

I ♥ SPK

How do you play with your Shopkins? Share your ideas here and check out how some other fans go silly for Shopville.

NAME THAT SHOPKIN CHALLENGE

POP ALL YOUR SHOPKINS IN A PILLOW CASE (OR YOU CAN FLICK THROUGH THEM ON THE WEBSITE). THE CHALLENGE IS TO PICK THEM OUT AND NAME THEM AND SAY WHICH SEASON THEY'RE FROM AS FAST AS YOU CAN!

CREATE A SHOPKINS SUPER-CHAIN

GRAB ALL OF YOUR SHOPKINS AND LAY THEM OUT ON A FLAT SURFACE. ORGANISE THEM INTO THEIR AISLE GROUPS, AND THEN LINE THEM UP IN ONE SUPER-LONG TWISTY LINE. HOW FAR DOES IT STRETCH?

RE-OPEN YOUR SHOPKINS!

KEEP YOUR BLIND BAGS AND POP YOUR SHOPKINS BACK IN. MIX THEM UP AND ENJOY THE SURPRISE ALL OVER AGAIN! YOU CAN EVEN TURN IT INTO A MATCHING GAME.

MAKE A DOUBLES NEST

DECORATE THE OUTSIDE OF AN EMPTY TISSUE BOX WITH COLOURFUL TISSUE PAPER AND STICKERS. TURN IT INTO A COMFY SNUG AND WHEN YOU GET A DOUBLE, POP THAT BUDDY INTO THE NEST!

SNAP SHOPKINS SELFIES

CREATE CUTE GROUPS OF YOUR SHOPKINS IN FUNNY LOCATIONS AND SNAP CLOSE-UP PICS, LIKE THEY'RE TAKING SELFIES! ADOOORABLE.

Who are your TOP 5 FAVE EVER SHOPKINS?
List them here.

1 _____
2 _____
3 _____
4 _____
5 _____

THE BEST GAMES I PLAY WITH MY SHOPKINS ARE ...

_____
_____
_____
_____

STYLE THE SHOPPIES

Dress up the Shoppies to match their personalities! Add some designs and patterns and then colour them cute.

POPETTE

A BOWL LOTTA FUN! LOUD AND LOVEABLE, IF THERE'S A CAMERA AROUND, POPETTE WILL POP UP! MOVIES ARE THIS SHOPPIE'S LIFE.

JESSICAKE

LIFE'S A PIECE OF CAKE FOR THIS LITTLE SWEETIE! SMART, SENSIBLE AND ALWAYS TASTEFULLY DRESSED, SHE LOVES A SHOPPING DAY.

BUBBLEISHA

WITH A SWEET 'N' SOUR PERSONALITY, THIS GIRL CAN REALLY BURST YOUR BUBBLE. SHE CAN GET INTO STICKY SITUATIONS, BUT IS REALLY AS SWEET AS CANDY.

PEPPA-MINT

SHE MAY LOOK CHILLED BUT PEPPA-MINT IS ALWAYS HAVING MELTDOWNS! MAYBE SHE KEEPS LOSING HER COOL BECAUSE SHE'S SO WARM HEARTED!

A Walk in the Park

It's a beautiful day in Shopville, and **Strawberry Kiss** is enjoying a warm walk in the park. Her quiet walk doesn't last for long … a moment later, she's soaked from head to foot with water! What has happened?

June Balloon and **Cheeky Chocolate** are also in the park.
"Hey, Strawberry, did you fall in the pond again?" asks June Balloon.
"No," replies Strawberry. She looks around and spots where the water has come from. "Milk Bud did!"

Milk Bud, the Petkin, has shaken himself dry and splashed the water all over Strawberry Kiss!

Apple Blossom comes running over.
"Milk Bud! I didn't mean that kind of shake!" she calls.
Apple Blossom is teaching Milk Bud new tricks.
She shows the other Shopkins what he has learned.
"Milk Bud, shake," she says to the adorable pup. This time, Milk Bud gets the trick right – he lifts a paw and shakes hands with Apple Blossom. Good boy, Milk Bud! The other Shopkins are very impressed – even Strawberry Kiss!

"What else can he do?" asks Cheeky Chocolate.
"He can do everything!" says Apple Blossom.
She shows the Shopkins all of their tricks.
Milk Bud can sit … he can roll over … he can
speak … and he can even speak French!

Apple Blossom tries something even trickier.
"Make a balloon animal!" she says to Milk Bud.
June Balloon squeals and giggles as Milk Bud tickles and twirls her into
a new shape. When he's finished, she looks like a cute balloon puppy!
She twists back into shape, and the whole gang cheers.

"And now, the most difficult trick of all," announces Apple Blossom.
"Fetch the stick!" she calls as she throws a stick deep into the park.
Milk Bud jumps up and down with excitement and scurries after the stick.

Milk Bud comes back with … Slick Breadstick!
"Close enough, I guess," giggles Apple Blossom. Perhaps they
need a little more practise on that one.

CHECK YA
LATER!

Shopkins™

SEASON 1

Once you shop...You can't stop!

148 TO COLLECT!

COLLECT THEM ALL!

TICK OFF YOUR COLLECTED SHOPKINS™ TO SEE WHICH ONES YOU STILL HAVE TO FIND!

***** LIMITED EDITION *****

Cupcake Queen	Buttercup	Tin 'a' Tuna	Twinky Winks	Papa Tomato	Sunny Screen
1-137	1-138	1-139	1-140	1-141	1-142

****** FRUIT & VEG *******

Apple Blossom	Rockin' Broc	Strawberry Kiss	Pineapple Crush	Melonie Pips	Miss Mushy-Moo	Posh Pear	Apple Blossom
1-001	1-002	1-003	1-004	1-005	1-006	1-007	1-008
Rockin' Broc	Strawberry Kiss	Pineapple Crush	Melonie Pips	Miss Mushy-Moo	Posh Pear		
1-009	1-010	1-011	1-012	1-013	1-014		

****** PANTRY *******

Tommy Ketchup	Nutty Butter	Peppe Pepper	Sally Shakes	Sugar Lump	Breaky Crunch	Alpha Soup	Gran Jam	Coolio
1-015	1-016	1-017	1-018	1-019	1-020	1-021	1-022	
Coolio	Tommy Ketchup	Nutty Butter	Peppe Pepper	Sally Shakes	Sugar Lump	Breaky Crunch	Alpha Soup	Gran Jam
1-023	1-024	1-025	1-026	1-027	1-028	1-029	1-030	1-031
								Coolio 1-032

****** BAKERY *******

Kooky Cookie	Bread Head	Creamy Bun-Bun	D'lish Donut	Cheese Kate	Mini Muffin	Flutter Cake	Kooky Cookie
1-033	1-034	1-035	1-036	1-037	1-038		
1-039	Bread Head 1-040	Creamy Bun-Bun 1-041	D'lish Donut 1-042	Cheese Kate 1-043	Mini Muffin 1-044	Flutter Cake 1-045	1-046

***** SWEET TREATS *****

Bubbles	Candy Kisses	Le'Quorice	Cheeky Chocolate	Candi Cotton	Lolli Poppins	Mandy Candy	Jelly B

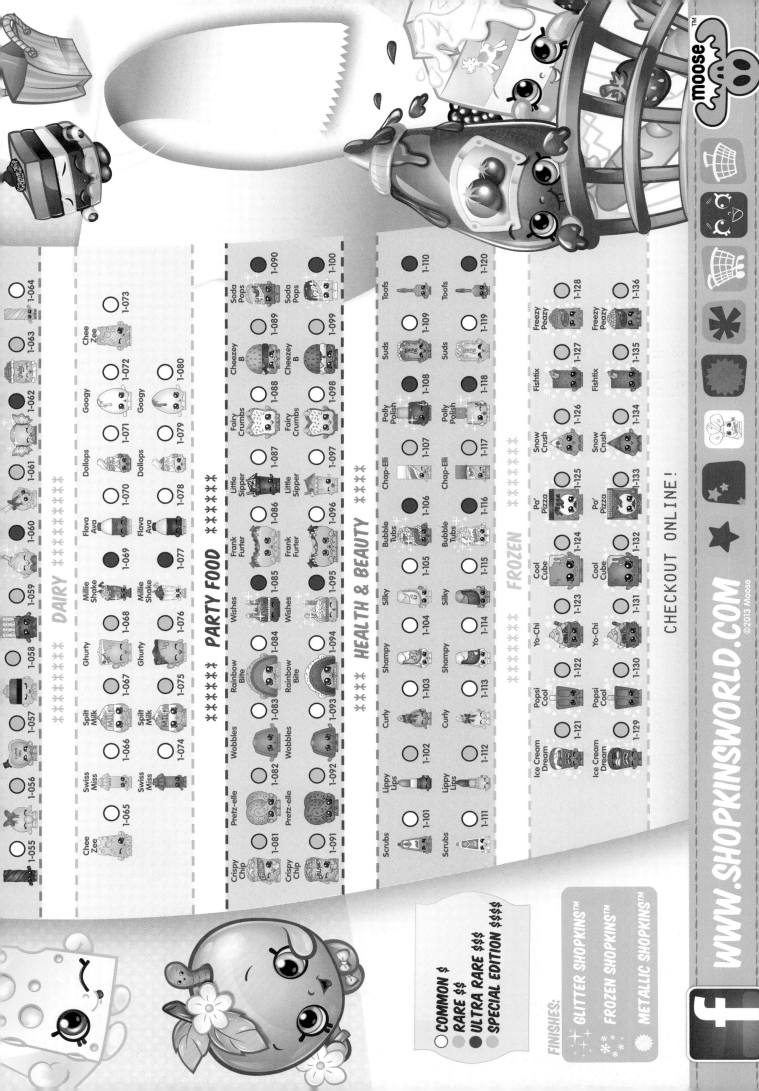

1-055 1-056 1-057 1-058 1-059 1-060 1-061 1-062 1-063 1-064

Chee Zee 1-065 Swiss Miss 1-066 Split Milk 1-067 Ghurty 1-068 1-069 Flava Ava 1-070 Dollops 1-071 Googy 1-072 Chee Zee 1-073

DAIRY ✸✸✸✸✸✸

Swiss Miss 1-074 Split Milk 1-075 Ghurty 1-076 1-077 Flava Ava 1-078 Dollops 1-079 Googy 1-080

✸✸✸✸✸ PARTY FOOD ✸✸✸✸✸✸

Crispy Chip 1-081 Pretz-elle 1-082 Wobbles 1-083 Rainbow Bite 1-084 1-085 Wishes 1-086 Frank Furter 1-087 Little Sipper 1-088 Fairy Crumbs 1-089 Cheezey B 1-090 Soda Pops

Crispy Chip 1-091 Pretz-elle 1-092 Wobbles 1-093 Rainbow Bite 1-094 1-095 Wishes 1-096 Frank Furter 1-097 Little Sipper 1-098 Fairy Crumbs 1-099 Cheezey B 1-100 Soda Pops

✸✸✸ HEALTH & BEAUTY ✸✸✸✸

Scrubs 1-101 Lippy Lips 1-102 Curly 1-103 Shampy 1-104 Silky 1-105 Bubble Tubs 1-106 Chap-Elli 1-107 Polly Polish 1-108 Suds 1-109 Toofs 1-110

Scrubs 1-111 Lippy Lips 1-112 Curly 1-113 Shampy 1-114 Silky 1-115 Bubble Tubs 1-116 Chap-Elli 1-117 Polly Polish 1-118 Suds 1-119 Toofs 1-120

✸✸✸✸✸✸✸ FROZEN ✸✸✸✸✸✸✸

Ice Cream Dream 1-121 Popsi Cool 1-122 Yo-Chi 1-123 Cool Cube 1-124 Pa' Pizza 1-125 Snow Crush 1-126 Fishtix 1-127 Freezy Peazy 1-128

Ice Cream Dream 1-129 Popsi Cool 1-130 Yo-Chi 1-131 Cool Cube 1-132 Pa' Pizza 1-133 Snow Crush 1-134 Fishtix 1-135 Freezy Peazy 1-136

CHECKOUT ONLINE!

WWW.SHOPKINSWORLD.COM

©2013 Moose

COMMON $
RARE $$
ULTRA RARE $$$
SPECIAL EDITION $$$$

FINISHES:
GLITTER SHOPKINS™ ✸
FROZEN SHOPKINS™ ✳
METALLIC SHOPKINS™ ❈

moose™

f

SEASON 2

Shopkins™

once you shop...You can't stop!

✳✳✳ CLEANING & LAUNDRY ✳✳✳

Dishy Liquid 2-087
Squeaky Clean 2-088
Wendy Washer 2-089
Bree Freshner 2-090

Molly Mops 2-091
Sweeps 2-092
Sarah Softner 2-093
Peta Plunger 2-094

Leafy 2-095
Dishy Liquid 2-096
Squeaky Clean 2-097
Wendy Washer 2-098

Bree Freshner 2-099
Molly Mops 2-100
Sweeps 2-101
Sarah Softner 2-102

Peta Plunger 2-103
Leafy 2-104

✳✳✳✳✳✳✳ BAKERY ✳✳✳✳✳✳✳

Slick Breadstick 2-035
Mary Muffin 2-036
Carrie Carrot Cake 2-037
Mary Meringue 2-038

Pecanna Pie 2-039
Choco Lava 2-040
Fifi Fruit Tart 2-041
Danni Danish 2-042

Cupcake Chic 2-043
Slick Breadstick 2-044
Mary Muffin 2-045
Carrie Carrot Cake 2-046

Mary Meringue 2-047
Pecanna Pie 2-048
Choco Lava 2-049
Fifi Fruit Tart 2-050

Danni Danish 2-051
Cupcake Chic 2-052

✳✳✳✳ SWEET TREATS ✳✳✳✳

Poppy Corn 2-053
Minnie Mintie 2-054
Banana Splitty 2-055
Yummy Gum 2-056

Waffle Sue 2-057
Ice-cream Dream 2-058
Cheery Churro 2-059
Pamela Pancake 2-060

Poppy Corn 2-061
Minnie Mintie 2-062
Banana Splitty 2-063
Yummy Gum 2-064

Waffle Sue 2-065
Ice-cream Dream 2-066
Cheery Churro 2-067
Pamela Pancake 2-068

HOMEWARES

- Toasty Pop 2-017
- Brenda Blender 2-018
- Coffee Drip 2-019
- Saucy Pan 2-020
- Ma Kettle 2-021
- Zappy Microwave 2-022
- Lisa Litter 2-023
- Lana Lamp 2-024
- Sizzles 2-025
- Toasty Pop 2-026
- Brenda Blender 2-027
- Coffee Drip 2-028
- Saucy Pan 2-029
- Ma Kettle 2-030
- Zappy Microwave 2-031
- Lisa Litter 2-032
- Lana Lamp 2-033
- Sizzles 2-034

LIMITED EDITION

- Marsha Mellow 2-137
- Rub-a-Glove 2-138
- Lenny Lime 2-139
- Lee Tea 2-140
- Donna Donut 2-141
- Angie Ankle Boot 2-142

FRUIT & VEG

- Chloe Flower 2-001
- Sour Lemon 2-002
- Juicy Orange 2-003
- Corny Cob 2-004
- Garlic Rose 2-005
- Boo-Hoo Onion 2-006
- Dippy Avocado 2-007
- Silly Chilli 2-008
- Chloe Flower 2-009
- Sour Lemon 2-010
- Juicy Orange 2-011
- Corny Cob 2-012
- Garlic Rose 2-013
- Boo-Hoo Onion 2-014
- Dippy Avocado 2-015
- Silly Chilli 2-016

BABY

- Dribbles 2-121
- Ga Ga Gourmet 2-122
- Dum Mee Mee 2-123
- Baby Swipes 2-124
- Sippy Sips 2-125
- Baby Puff 2-126
- Nappy Dee 2-127
- Shampoo Sue 2-128
- Dribbles 2-129
- Ga Ga Gourmet 2-130
- Dum Mee Mee 2-131
- Baby Swipes 2-132
- Sippy Sips 2-133
- Baby Puff 2-134
- Nappy Dee 2-135
- Shampoo Sue 2-136

PANTRY

- Fi Fi Flour 2-069
- Bart Beans 2-070
- Fasta Pasta 2-071
- Olivia Oil 2-072
- Honeeey 2-073
- Al Foil 2-074
- Toffy Coffee 2-075
- Cornell Mustard 2-076
- Chris P Crackers 2-077
- Fi Fi Flour 2-078
- Bart Beans 2-079
- Fasta Pasta 2-080
- Olivia Oil 2-081
- Honeeey 2-082
- Al Foil 2-083
- Toffy Coffee 2-084
- Cornell Mustard 2-085
- Chris P Crackers 2-086

SHOES

- Prommy 2-105
- Sneaky Sue 2-106
- Heels 2-107
- Sneaky Wedge 2-108
- Betty Boot 2-109
- Wedgy Wendy 2-110
- Bun Bun Slipper 2-111
- Cute Boot 2-112
- Prommy 2-113
- Sneaky Sue 2-114
- Heels 2-115
- Sneaky Wedge 2-116
- Betty Boot 2-117
- Wedgy Wendy 2-118
- Bun Bun Slipper 2-119
- Cute Boot 2-120

COLLECT THEM ALL!

CHECKOUT ONLINE! WWW.SHOPKINSWORLD.COM

SMALL MART RACE

The Fruit & Veg gang have decided to have a race! Who will make it across the store and back to their aisle first?

PLAY this board game to find out!

START

1

2

3
Bread Head stops you for a chat. Miss a turn.

17

16

15

14

13
BAKERY

18

19

20
Frost T Fridge wants to chill out. Miss a turn.

21

FINISH
FRUIT & VEG

32

31
HOMEWARES

30
Zappy Microwave shares a speedy trick. Move forward 3 spaces.

HOW TO PLAY

- Use Shopkins Fruit & Veg characters as your counters.
- Find a dice and roll it to begin. Whoever gets the highest number starts.
- Take turns rolling the dice and moving that number of squares across the board.
- If you land on a marked square, follow the directions.
- Whoever gets to the Fruit & Veg aisle first is the winner!

4

5

6

7

8

12

11

10
Mary Meringue distracts another player. Jump ahead 3 spaces.

9
SWEET TREATS

15

22
Al Foil shows you a short cut. Move on 2 spaces.

23
PANTRY

24

25

29

28
Uh-oh, you slip on Ice Cream Dream's spill. Move back 4 spaces.

27

26

SEASON 3

Shopkins™
Once you shop...You can't stop!

COMMON
RARE
ULTRA RARE
SPECIAL EDITION

FINISHES:
CHOC FROSTED SHOPKINS™
POLISHED PEARL SHOPKINS™
COOL JEWELS SHOPKINS™

✶✶✶✶✶ HOMEWARES

Washa 3-103	Vicky Vac 3-104	Frost T Fridge 3-105	Blow-Anne 3-106	
Teenie TV 3-107	Radio Sue 3-108	Chatter 3-109	Mobile Mary 3-110	
Mixie & Maxie 3-111	Washa 3-112	Vicky Vac 3-113	Frost T Fridge 3-114	
Blow-Anne 3-115	Teenie TV 3-116	Radio Sue 3-117	Chatter 3-118	
Mobile Mary 3-119	Mixie & Maxie 3-120			

✶✶✶✶✶ SWEET TREATS ✶✶✶✶✶

PopRock 3-051	Cream E Cookie 3-052	Macca Roon 3-053	Chocky Box 3-054
Wanda Wafer 3-055	Choc Kiss 3-056	Suzie Sundae 3-057	Candy Apple 3-058
Ginger Fred 3-059	PopRock 3-060	Cream E Cookie 3-061	Macca Roon 3-062
Chocky Box 3-063	Wanda Wafer 3-064	Choc Kiss 3-065	Suzie Sundae 3-066
Candy Apple 3-067	Ginger Fred 3-068		

✶✶✶✶✶ BAKERY ✶✶✶✶✶✶✶

Cheese Louise 3-001	Queen of Tarts 3-002	Patty Cake 3-003	Lana Banana Bread 3-004
Toastie Bread 3-005	Candy Cookie 3-006	Birthday Betty 3-007	Wendy Wedding Cake 3-008
Nilla Slice 3-009	Cheese Louise 3-010	Queen of Tarts 3-011	Patty Cake 3-012
Lana Banana Bread 3-013	Toastie Bread 3-014	Candy Cookie 3-015	Birthday Betty 3-016
Wendy Wedding Cake 3-017	Nilla Slice 3-018		

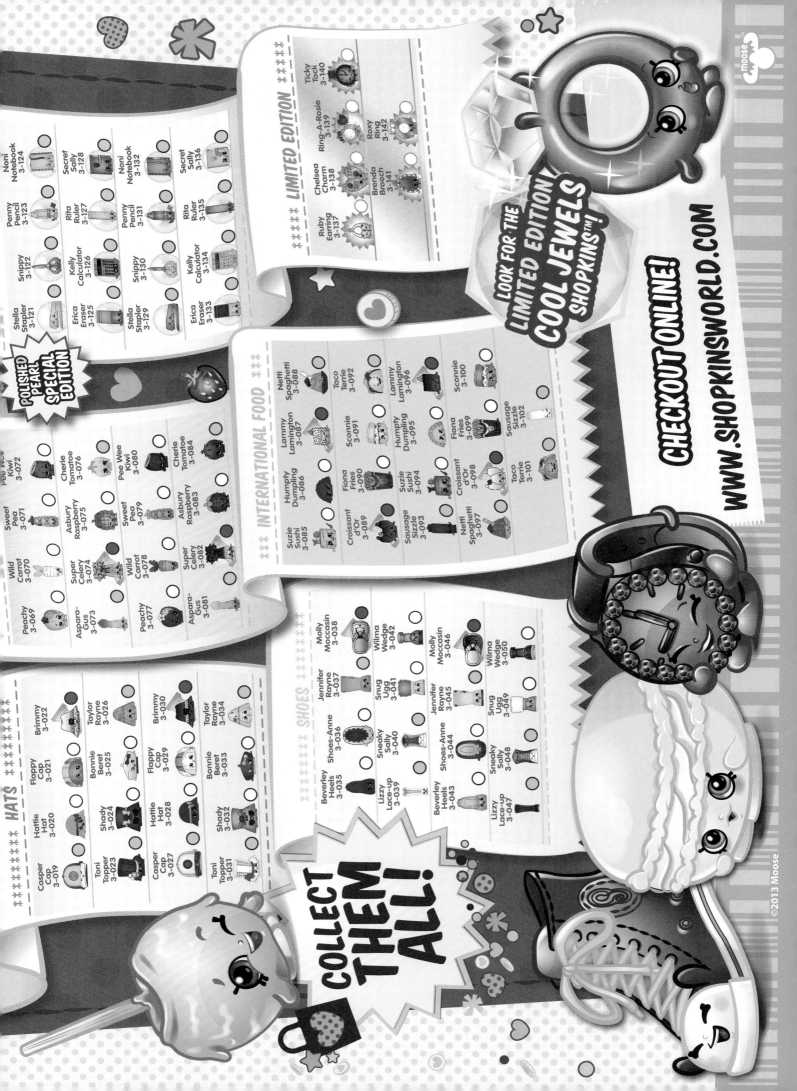

POLISHED PEARL SPECIAL EDITION

✶✶✶✶✶ LIMITED EDITION ✶✶✶✶✶

| Ruby Earring 3-137 | Chelsea Charm 3-138 | Ring-A-Rosie 3-139 | Ticky Tock 3-140 |
| Brenda Brooch 3-141 | Roxy Ring 3-142 |

LOOK FOR THE LIMITED EDITION COOL JEWELS SHOPKINS™!

CHECKOUT ONLINE!
WWW.SHOPKINSWORLD.COM

Stationery

Stella Stapler 3-121	Snippy 3-122	Penny Pencil 3-123	Noni Notebook 3-124
Erica Eraser 3-125	Kelly Calculator 3-126	Rita Ruler 3-127	Secret Sally 3-128
Stella Stapler 3-129	Snippy 3-130	Penny Pencil 3-131	Noni Notebook 3-132
Erica Eraser 3-133	Kelly Calculator 3-134	Rita Ruler 3-135	Secret Sally 3-136

Vegetables / Fruit

Peachy 3-069	Wild Carrot 3-070	Sweet Pea 3-071	Pee Wee Kiwi 3-072
Aspara-Gus 3-073	Super Celery 3-074	Asbury Raspberry 3-075	Cherie Tomatoe 3-076
Peachy 3-077	Wild Carrot 3-078	Sweet Pea 3-079	Pee Wee Kiwi 3-080
Aspara-Gus 3-081	Super Celery 3-082	Asbury Raspberry 3-083	Cherie Tomatoe 3-084

✶✶✶ INTERNATIONAL FOOD ✶✶✶

Suzie Sushi 3-085	Humpy Dumpling 3-086	Lammy Lamington 3-087	Netti Spaghetti 3-088
Croissant d'Or 3-089	Fiona Fries 3-090	Sconnie 3-091	Taco Terrie 3-092
Sausage Sizzle 3-093	Suzie Sushi 3-094	Humpy Dumpling 3-095	Lammy Lamington 3-096
Netti Spaghetti 3-097	Croissant d'Or 3-098	Fiona Fries 3-099	Sconnie 3-100
Taco Terrie 3-101	Sausage Sizzle 3-102

✶✶✶✶✶✶✶ HATS ✶✶✶✶✶✶✶

Casper Cap 3-019	Hattie Hat 3-020	Flappy Cap 3-021	Brimmy 3-022
Toni Topper 3-023	Shady 3-024	Bonnie Beret 3-025	Taylor Rayne 3-026
Casper Cap 3-027	Hattie Hat 3-028	Flappy Cap 3-029	Brimmy 3-030
Toni Topper 3-031	Shady 3-032	Bonnie Beret 3-033	Taylor Rayne 3-034

✶✶✶✶✶✶ SHOES ✶✶✶✶✶✶

Beverley Heels 3-035	Shoes-Anne 3-036	Jennifer Rayne 3-037	Molly Moccasin 3-038
Lizzy Lace-up 3-039	Sneaky Sally 3-040	Snug Ugg 3-041	Wilma Wedge 3-042
Beverley Heels 3-043	Shoes-Anne 3-044	Jennifer Rayne 3-045	Molly Moccasin 3-046
Lizzy Lace-up 3-047	Sneaky Sally 3-048	Snug Ugg 3-049	Wilma Wedge 3-050

COLLECT THEM ALL!

SEASON 4

Shopkins™

Once you shop...you can't stop!

LOOK OUT FOR NEW PETKINS!

FINISHES:
- SHIMMY SHOPKINS™
- PETKINS SHOPKINS™
- PERFUME PRETTIES SHOPKINS™

- ○ COMMON
- ● RARE
- ● ULTRA RARE
- ● SPECIAL EDITION
- ● LIMITED EDITION

✓ TICK AS YOU COLLECT!

✱✱✱ PETSHOP ✱✱✱✱✱✱

Doggy Bowl 4-073	Little Pet Collar 4-074	Dennis Ball 4-075	Pup-E-House 4-076	
Kitty Catbed 4-077	Teena Catfood 4-078	Goldie Fish Bowl 4-079	Pup E Brush 4-080	
Doggy Bowl 4-081	Little Pet Collar 4-082	Dennis Ball 4-083	Pup-E-House 4-084	
Kitty Catbed 4-085	Teena Catfood 4-086	Goldie Fish Bowl 4-087	Pup-E-Brush 4-088	

✱✱✱ GARDEN

✱✱✱✱✱✱✱ PETKINS ✱✱✱✱✱✱✱✱

Jilly Jam 4-089	Tracey Tomato 4-090	Shy Pie/ Cherry pie 4-091	Jilly Jam 4-092
Tracey Tomato 4-093	Shy Pie/ Cherry pie 4-094	Milk Bud 4-095	Tubby Butter 4-096
Hot Choc 4-097	Milk Bud 4-098	Tubby Butter 4-099	Hot Choc 4-100
Big Topping 4-101	Mabel Syrup 4-102	Ice Cream Cup 4-103	Big Topping 4-104
Mabel Syrup 4-105	Ice Cream Cup 4-106	Bobby Sock 4-107	Jingle Purse 4-108

✱✱✱✱✱ FRUIT & VEG ✱✱✱✱✱✱

Kris P Lettuce 4-001	Peely Potato 4-002	Milly Mushroom 4-003	Cheeky Cherries 4-004
April Apricot 4-005	Kris P Lettuce 4-006	Peely Potato 4-007	Milly Mushroom 4-008
	Cheeky Cherries 4-009	April Apricot 4-010	

✱✱✱✱✱✱ BAKERY ✱✱✱✱✱✱

Bread Crumbs 4-011	Cookie Nut 4-012	Cindy Bon 4-013	Bagel Billy 4-014

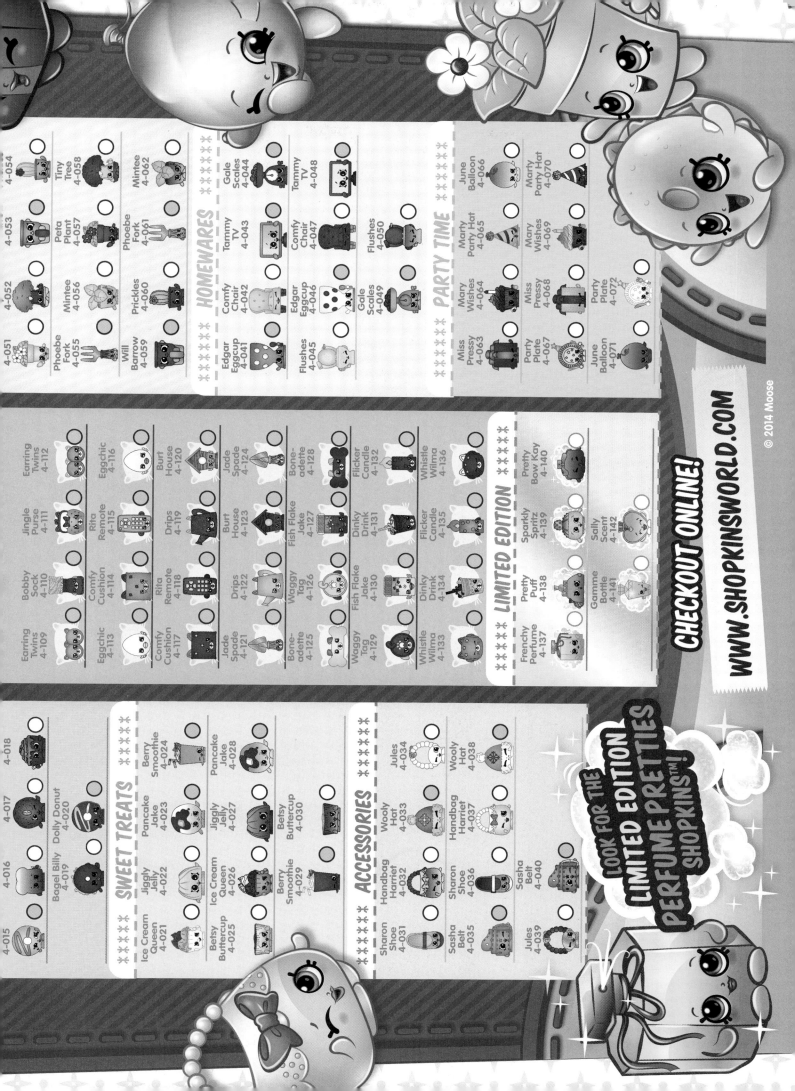

HOMEWARES
Edgar Eggcup 4-041 · Comfy Chair 4-042 · Tammy TV 4-043 · Gale Scales 4-044
Flushes 4-045 · Edgar Eggcup 4-046 · Comfy Chair 4-047 · Tammy TV 4-048
Gale Scales 4-049 · Flushes 4-050

4-051 · 4-052 · 4-053 · 4-054
Phoebe Fork 4-055 · Mintee 4-056 · Peta Plant 4-057 · Tiny Tree 4-058
Will Barrow 4-059 · Prickles 4-060 · Phoebe Fork 4-061 · Mintee 4-062

PARTY TIME
Miss Pressy 4-063 · Mary Wishes 4-064 · Mary Party Hat 4-065 · June Balloon 4-066
Party Plate 4-067 · Miss Pressy 4-068 · Mary Wishes 4-069 · Marty Party Hat 4-070
June Balloon 4-071 · Party Plate 4-072

Earring Twins 4-109 · Bobby Sock 4-110 · Jingle Purse 4-111 · Earring Twins 4-112
Eggchic 4-113 · Comfy Cushion 4-114 · Rita Remote 4-115 · Eggchic 4-116
Comfy Cushion 4-117 · Rita Remote 4-118 · Drips 4-119 · Burt House 4-120
Jade Spade 4-121 · Drips 4-122 · Burt House 4-123 · Jade Spade 4-124
Bone-adette 4-125 · Waggy Tag 4-126 · Fish Flake Jake 4-127 · Bone-adette 4-128
Fish Flake Jake 4-129 · Fish Flake Jake 4-130 · Dinky Drink 4-131 · Flicker Candle 4-132
Whistle Wilma 4-133 · Dinky Drink 4-134 · Flicker Candle 4-135 · Whistle Wilma 4-136

LIMITED EDITION
Frenchy Perfume 4-137 · Pretty Puff 4-138 · Sparkly Spritz 4-139 · Pretty Bow Kay 4-140
Gamme Bottle 4-141 · Sally Scent 4-142

4-015 · 4-016 · 4-017 · 4-018
Bagel Billy 4-019 · Dolly Donut 4-020

SWEET TREATS
Ice Cream Queen 4-021 · Jiggly Jelly 4-022 · Pancake Jake 4-023 · Berry Smoothie 4-024
Betsy Buttercup 4-025 · Ice Cream 4-026 · Jiggly Jelly 4-027 · Pancake Jake 4-028
Berry Smoothie 4-029 · Betsy Buttercup 4-030

ACCESSORIES
Sharon Shoe 4-031 · Handbag Harriet 4-032 · Wooly Hat 4-033 · Jules 4-034
Sasha Belt 4-035 · Sharon Shoe 4-036 · Handbag Harriet 4-037 · Wooly Hat 4-038
Jules 4-039 · Sasha Belt 4-040

CHECKOUT ONLINE!
WWW.SHOPKINSWORLD.COM

LOOK FOR THE LIMITED EDITION PERFUME PRETTIES SHOPKINS™!

SHOPPIES SPOTTING

PEPPA-MINT AND THE OTHER SHOPPIES ARE HAVING AN AMAZING DAY OUT WITH THEIR SHOPKIN BFFS!

THESE SEASON 4 SHOPKINS HAVE SNEAKED INTO THE SCENE. CAN YOU SPOT THEM?

CAN YOU FIND THESE LITTLE PICTURES IN THE BIG SCENE? TICK THEM AS YOU FIND THEM.

55

HOMEWARE REPAIR

These awesome Shopkins need some close-up repairs.
Can you match the characters to their names?

1

2

3

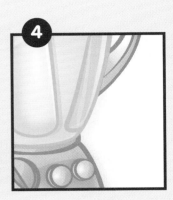
4

BRENDA BLENDER   VICKY VAC

TOASTY POP   FROST T FRIDGE

BABY NAMES

Aw, too cute! Can you unscramble the names of these
Baby Shopkins? Then match them to their pictures.

1 PABBYFUF _ _ _ _ _ _ _ _   **3** BIRDSELB _ _ _ _ _ _ _ _

2 DEPANPYE _ _ _ _ _ _ _ _   **4** SSYPPPIIS _ _ _ _ _ _ _ _ _

5 YBWABESIPS _ _ _ _ _ _ _ _ _ _

a

b

c

d

e
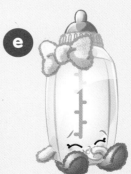

ANSWERS ON PAGE 93

SMALL MART CHECKOUT

Who's the missing character in each row?

1    ?

a

2    ?

b

3  ?

c

EGGCHIC FOR REAL

Which picture is the real Eggchic?
All of the others have had some pretty strange changes!

1

2

3

4

5

6

ANSWERS ON PAGE 93

MATCHING BUDDIES

The Shopkins are all mixed up! None of the characters are sitting next to their doubles. Can you draw lines to pair up the buddies?

Which character doesn't have a match?

CARRIED-AWAY COLOURING

This little cutie loves having a carry on with her friends.
Can you give her a fashionable splash of colour?

I'M ALWAYS OUT TO BAG A BARGAIN!

Colour Harriet in her usual hot pink or blue – or give her a brand-new look!

MEET SEASON 3

PEACHY
She always gives you a warm, fuzzy feeling when you meet her.

♥s chillin' out with Ice Cream Dream.

SWEET PEA
Cute and cosy, and ready to pop out of their pod.

♥s juggling.

BAKERY

CHEESE LOUISE
A cool little mover. When it comes to being smooth, she takes the cake!

♥s telling cheesy jokes to her friends.

PATTY CAKE
A real frost-top who loves to sprinkle joy wherever she goes.

♥s speed-baking!

TOASTIE BREAD
Warm at heart with a very dry sense of humour.

♥s surprising Toasty Pop when he least expects it!

SWEET TREATS

SUZIE SUNDAE
She's nuts about ice cream and can whip up a yummy treat in seconds.

♥s relaxing on a sundae.

MACCA ROON
A bit of an airhead, but one of the sweetest Shopkins you'll ever meet.

♥s getting a new colour put in!

CANDY APPLE
When she starts something, she sticks with it.

♥s playing fiddle sticks.

INTERNATIONAL FOOD

TACO TERRIE
This Tex Mex is full of beans and can go a bit over the top!

♥s dancing around sombreros.

NETTI SPAGHETTI
Long and thin, and she loves to spin!

♥s twirling in ballet classes.

HOMEWARES

CHATTER
Loves to have a chat and
is a very good listener.
❤s talking, talking, talking.

FROST T FRIDGE
A cool chic who loves to chill out, but
can get a little frosty sometimes.
❤s making icy poles.

STATIONERY

PENNY PENCIL
Always has a point to make
and likes to leave her mark.
❤s writing and drawing.

ERICA ERASER
A real problem solver who
loves to right wrongs.
❤s performing magic –
to make things disappear!

SECRET SALLY
Trustworthy and faithful, she
will always keep your secrets.
❤s playing hide and secret!

SHOES

SNEAKY SALLY
A real sneaky mover with a bouncy personality.
❤s being a step ahead of her friends.

JENNIFER RAYNE
Always up to her ankles in trouble,
and loves to splash out on her friends.
❤s splashing in puddles.

HATS

CASPER CAP
The Shopkin who can cap off any outfit
and is always in peak condition.
❤s playing baseball.

TAYLOR RAYNE
A little wet behind the ears, but very loyal.
She'll always cover for you!
❤s splashing in puddles.

ROXY RING

Always has a sparkle in her eye
and is a cut above the rest.
♥ s attending weddings.

RING-A-ROSIE

Likes to get attached.
Once she's on your finger,
she won't let go.
♥ s playing piano.

TICKY TOCK

It takes time to get to know
her, but once you do, the
seconds will fly by.
♥ s watching time go by.

CHELSEA CHARM

Has a strong heart and will be
your bestie forever.
♥ s hanging with her BFF.

RUBY EARRING

A stylish earring who hangs out
with the beautiful people.
♥ s having lobes of fun!

BRENDA BROOCH

Likes to be worn, but she never looks
tired. She shines at any occasion.
♥ s dinner parties with friends.

EXCLUSIVES

HEELY

Loves to walk the catwalk, but her real dream is to make it big in shoe-biz!

❤ s going to the theatre.

KELLY JELLY

Enjoys hotfooting it to the beach on a sunny day to feel the sand between her straps.

❤ s walking on the beach.

MINDY MIRROR

Always in a reflective mood, she's compact but has a big personality.

❤ s checking herself out!

BLUSHY BRUSH

She may always turn red, but she is very good at covering up how she really feels.

❤ s brushing up on her dance lessons.

WALLY WATER

He likes to be crystal clear when explaining things. A real cool dude!

❤ s doing triathlons.

KYLIE CONE

Can waffle on for hours about how cool she is, but becomes a mess when the heat is on!

❤ s snowball fights.

QUILTY BOOT

Likes to live life in the fast lane but she's really made for style rather than speed.

❤ s snuggling up in front of a fireplace.

PENNY PURSE

Some Shopkins think she's made of money but she's a real penny pincher.

❤ s counting her pennies.

63

YOU + ME = BEST FRIENDS

FRIEND FILE FOR YOU

ABOUT ME

Favourite colour: Gold

A word/phrase I use ALL the time: OK

Favourite hobby:

I would love to be a: police woman

Favourite Shopkin: H eels

Because she is prtty

Favourite Petkin:

Because

My favourite Shoppie is:

Because

ABOUT MY BFF

Favourite colour:

A word/phrase he/she uses ALL the time:

Favourite hobby:

He/she would love to be a:

Favourite Shopkin:

Because

Favourite Petkin:

Because

My favourite Shoppie is:

Because

Make sure this page is covered when your friend fills in her side. No cheeky peeks!

Friendship is super important to the Shopkins. How well do you and your BFF know each other? Take turns to fill out one side of this friend file each and then check your match-up success!

FRIEND FILE FOR YOUR FRIEND

ABOUT MY BFF

Favourite colour: _____

A word/phrase he/she uses ALL the time: _____

_____

Favourite hobby: *badminton*

He/she would love to be a: *badminton*

Favourite Shopkin: _____

Because _____

Favourite Petkin: _____

Because _____

My favourite Shoppie is: _____

Because _____

Now check your answers and see how many match-ups you get!

ABOUT ME

Favourite colour: _____

A word/phrase I use ALL the time: _____

Favourite hobby: _____

I would love to be a: _____

Favourite Shopkin: _____

Because _____

Favourite Petkin: _____

Because _____

My favourite Shoppie is: _____

Because _____

MY SHOPKINS STORY

**Do you love hearing what the Shopkins are up to in the aisles?
Now you can write your own teeny tale!**

SEE HOW MANY OF THESE CHARACTERS YOU CAN FIT IN YOUR STORY:

SECRET SALLY **TACO TERRIE** **CASPER CAP** **QUILTY BOOT** **JENNIFER RAYNE**

HAPPY WRITING.
AND IF YOU MAKE
A MISTAKE, NO
PROBLEM!

ANSWERS ON PAGE 93

SHOPKINS SQUARES

How good are your Shopkin-spotting skills?
Find where these five sequences appear in the big grid!

1

2

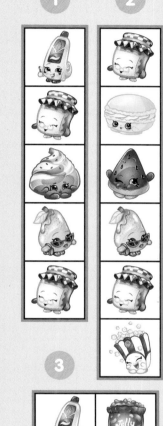

3

4

5

THIS PUZZLE
IS A-MAIZ-ING!

STRAWBERRY KISS SMOOTHIE

This special smoothie is a perfect treat for hungry tummies! And it has a secret ingredient that you might just love ...

LET'S DAYDREAM UP THE PERFECT SHAKE ...

INGREDIENTS

- 2 bananas, cut into chunks
- A handful of chopped strawberries
- Small tub of natural yoghurt
- Optional: 2 ice cubes
- Secret ingredient: 1 tablespoon of chocolate syrup!

TRY ADDING BLUEBERRIES - THEY'LL MAKE IT GOOD ENOUGH TO SHARE!

- Ask an adult to help you combine all of the ingredients in a blender.
- Blend until smooth.
- Serve in a tall glass with a single chopped strawberry to decorate.
- You can experiment with different fruits!

BRENDA BLENDER IS A WHIZ AT BLENDING UP SMOOTHIES! DOODLE AS MANY DIFFERENT KINDS OF FRUIT AS YOU CAN THINK OF SO SHE CAN MIX UP LOTS OF NEW RECIPES.

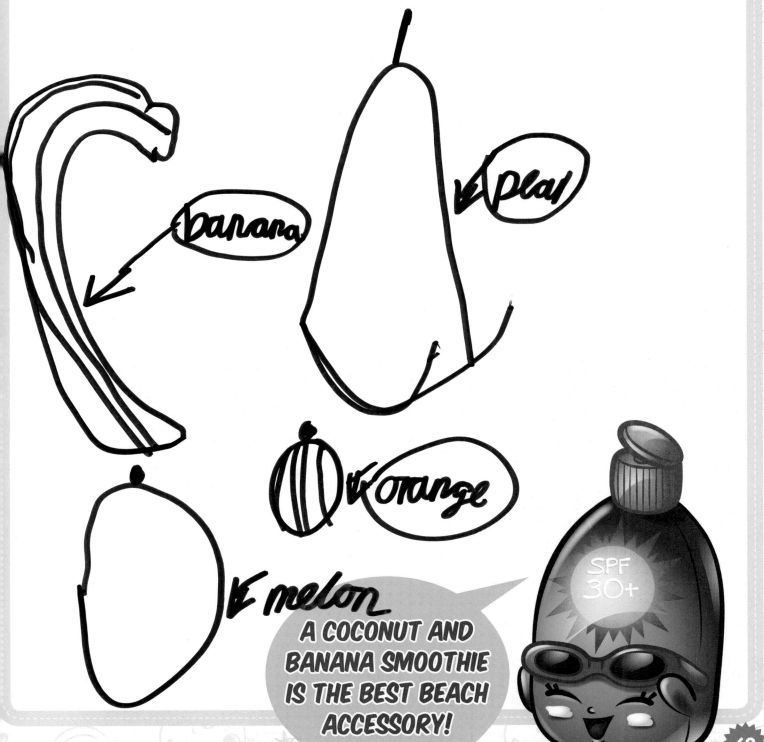

banana

play

orange

melon

A COCONUT AND BANANA SMOOTHIE IS THE BEST BEACH ACCESSORY!

NAME GAME

Can you work out the letter that connects these Shopkin names?
Write it in the heart each time. Fill in the rest of the missing letters too!

1 HOT CHO ♥ HEEKY CHERRIES

2 PANCAKE JAK ♥ GGCHIC

3 CUPC_KE CHI ♥ OMFY CH_IR

4 F_F_ FR_IT TAR ♥ ACO TE_RI

5 DRI_ _LE ♥ I_ _LES

6 _ENN_FER RA_N ♥ RICA E_ASE_

7 R_ _Y _ _ _ N ♥ R_N J_M

8 I_ _ C_E_M D_EA ♥ I_ _IE MI_ _I_

IT GETS
TRICKIER AS
YOU GO DOWN,
BECAUSE EVEN
MORE LETTERS
ARE MISSING!

70

ANSWERS ON PAGE 93

IN A LATHER

Shampy and Silky are at their most stylish when they're together!
Help Shampy through the bubbly maze to find her Season 1 bestie.

START

HOW MANY COINS DOES SHAMPY PASS ALONG THE WAY?

FINISH

DONUT DIFFERENCES!
SUPER-SWEET DONATINA USUALLY ENDS UP EATING MORE DONUTS THAN SHE SELLS! CAN YOU SPOT 8 DIFFERENCES BETWEEN THE PICTURES BEFORE SHE GOBBLES THIS BOX?

COLOUR A DONUT FOR EACH DIFFERENCE YOU SPOT.

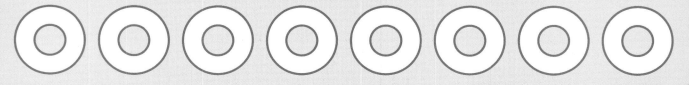

ANSWERS ON PAGE 93

READY TO SHOP!

THE SHOPPIES ALL HAVE THEIR OWN SENSE OF STYLE — AND YOU CAN SEE THAT IN THEIR SHADOWS! CAN YOU MATCH EACH SHOPPIE TO THEIR SHADOW SHAPE?

Peppa-mint

Jessicake

Popette

Bubbleisha

Donatina

1

2

3

4

WHOSE SHADOW IS MISSING?

 WHICH SHOPPIE IS READY FOR A SHOPPING TRIP AND WAITING FOR THE OTHERS? CIRCLE EVERY THIRD LETTER AND THEN UNSCRAMBLE THOSE LETTERS TO FIND OUT.

B D S P M I O T K E A E P T C M B J C S S H N E U O A

_ _ _ _ _ _ _ _ _

BUDDY COLOUR-UP

Whether he's pink or blue, Milk Bud is always super-cute.
Add a splash of colour to make him 'Moo' with happiness!

ANSWERS ON PAGE 93

CATCH THE PETKINS

How quickly can you find all 10 Season 4 Petkins in the grid?
Set your watch and time yourself – ticking them as you go.

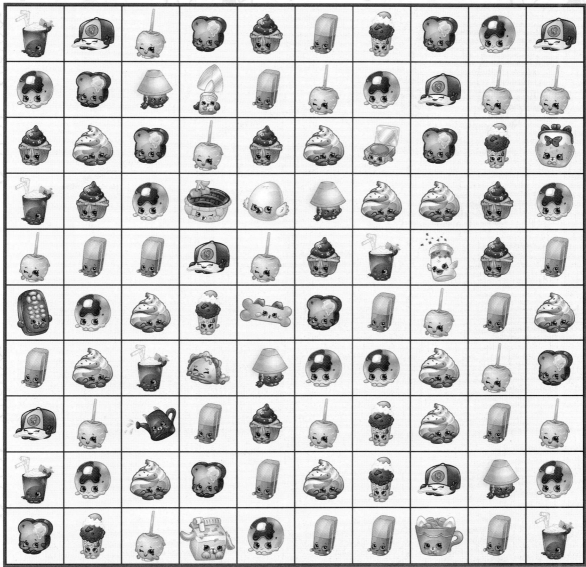

CAN YOUR FRIENDS BEAT YOUR TIME? HEE, HEE!

SHOPKINS SLEEPOVER

SWEET SNACKETTES
GO CUPCAKE CHIC!

Make Cupcake Chic really happy and decorate your own cupcakes with icing and multi-coloured sprinkles. You can present them on a colourful cake stand and, as an extra treat, you could pop blind bags on top with an adorable Shopkin hiding inside for each person.

SHOPKINS TREATS

CREATE JARS OF YUMMY SNACKS BASED ON YOUR FAVE CHARACTERS.

Little pretzel bites for Pretz-elle, lollipops for Lolli Poppins, mini chocolate bars for Cheeky Chocolate, jelly beans for Jelly B, and so on. You can stick a picture of the character on the jar to complete the super-cute effect.

MOVIE MAGIC
POPPY CORN IS ALWAYS FIRST IN LINE FOR A GOOD FILM!

Get some bowls of her favourite buttery snack and get your friends and all of your Shopkins round for the ultimate movie night.

INVITES AND DECORATIONS

Photocopy or scan this adorable invite to send to your friends, or draw your own version!

If you're not very crafty, there are also loads of free printables online for invites, bottle labels, table place names and more.

DEAR

....

YOU'RE INVITED TO MY SHOPKINS SLEEPOVER!

ON .... AT ....

PLEASE BRING A SLEEPING BAG
AND YOUR SHOPKINS SWAPKINS!

CHECK YA LATER!   FROM ....

CRAZY GAMES

WHICH SHOPKIN AM I?

Pop all of your Shopkins into a pillow case. Each player takes a turn to pick a Shopkin out of the case. The aim is for the rest of the players to guess which character they are – but you can only ask questions with a 'yes' or 'no' answer! For example, 'Is she in the Bakery aisle?' or 'Is he from Season 1?'. Remember to work as a team.

SLEEPING BAG SWAPKINS

Take turns to be the 'Limited Edition' character. That person should leave the room while the rest of the players hide in each other's sleeping bags. When the Limited Edition character comes back everybody should disguise their voice and say 'Check ya later' one by one. If they guess the right person, that person becomes the Limited Edition character and the game starts again.

FEATURES

SHOPPER STYLE

WHAT KIND OF SHOPPING BESTIE ARE YOU? TICK ALL THE STATEMENTS THAT APPLY TO YOU THEN COUNT UP YOUR ANSWERS TO FIND OUT.

♥ Shopping in the sales is the best.

♥ I always see too many things that I want.

♥ I'm good at spotting things for my friends.

♥ I find things that others miss.

✦ I love doing makeovers on my friends.

✦ People often comment on what I wear.

✦ I love trying on clothes.

✦ I often doodle outfit ideas.

★ I don't follow fashions.

★ I love to look different to my friends.

★ Shopping should be fun, not fast.

★ I like making my own accessories.

MOSTLY PINK
SUPER-QUICK BARGAIN SPOTTER!

MOSTLY PURPLE
FASHION STYLIST OF THE FUTURE!

MOSTLY YELLOW
CREATIVE AND DREAMY BROWSER!

NOW DRAW YOURSELF AS A SHOPPIE AND FILL IN YOUR CHARACTER PROFILE.

MY SHOPPING STYLE IS: _____

SHOPPIE NAME: _____

HAIR COLOUR: _____

ACCESSORIES: _____

SHOPKIN BESTIES: _____

79

STORY TIME!

No Pain, No Gain

Cheeky Chocolate is on a mission! He's running on the conveyor belt at the Small Mart checkout as fast as he can. But why?

"Hey Cheeky," calls **Suzie Sundae**, "I think you're, like, running in the wrong direction."

"I'm training for the Shopkins Olympics!" shouts Cheeky.

Cheeky wants to be the marathon champion of Shopville!

Toasty Pops has other ideas.

"I'm way faster than you, Cheeky," he says. "I can toast a bagel in ten seconds flat!"

"Uh, I don't know if that's, like, the same thing, Toasty," replies Suzie.

Cheeky Chocolate doesn't think Toasty can ever beat him. He challenges Toasty to a race! **Milk Bud** decides to join in too, just for fun. The Shopkins line up on the conveyor belts, and Suzie prepares to start the race. The last Shopkin standing will be the winner.

"Um, like, go!" Suzie calls.

The conveyor belts rumble around and Cheeky and Toasty start running. Cheeky has a sneaky idea. He grabs a dog treat from the conveyor belt and throws it towards Toasty.

"Fetch!" he calls. Milk Bud spots the treat and jumps for it … landing on top of Toasty and knocking him over!

"Yes! I am the marathon champion!" shouts Cheeky.

Toasty jumps over next to Cheeky's conveyor belt. He picks up a checkout divider and drops it in front of Cheeky.

"Woa, Toasty, what are you doing?" says Cheeky.

"I'm making you the hurdle champion, too," says Toasty, with a smile. Cheeky can't keep up and trips over the hurdle and crashes into a bucket on the floor.

"You deserve to be the champ, Cheeky," says Toasty. "No pain, no gain!" The Shopkins all giggle – apart from Cheeky!

CROSS IT OUT

Cross out all the As, Fs, Ms and Ys to reveal the name of Erica Eraser's BFF. The first one has been done for you.

P	A	E	F	N	F	A	Y	A
M	F	N	Y	M	Y	P	A	F
Y	E	A	N	C	A	M	F	A
A	F	Y	I	F	F	A	L	M

SNEAKY GAMES

Sneaky Wedge can be a bit mischievous, but he also has a straight-laced, go-getter side! Unscramble the letters in the blue footprints to discover the answer to his question.

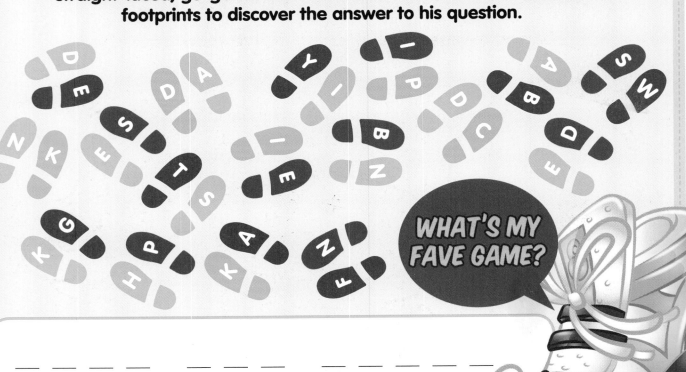

WHAT'S MY FAVE GAME?

ANSWERS ON PAGE 93

SHOPKINS SWAPKINS!

The Shopkins need to be matched up to their other halves.
Can you help? Draw lines to match the pairs.

ICE ME UP!

Decorate these baked treats so they're sweet as can be!

MEET SEASON 4

APRIL APRICOT
Fun and fruity, but trouble follows her
and she usually ends up in a jam.
♥ s ripening!

CHEEKY CHERRIES
Cheeky and cheery, when they put their
heads together they can do anything!
♥ s finishing off each other's sentences.

BAKERY

BAGEL BILLY
Not just a roll with a hole!
He's bagelicious and always filling good.
♥ s letting the good times roll!

ICE CREAM QUEEN
Never cold to her loyal followers, she
likes to sprinkle her friendship around.
♥ s practicing her Royal 'Wafer'.

PANCAKE JAKE
A stack of fun and totally pantastic! Will
flip over backwards to help you out.
♥ s playing Frisbee.

SWEET
TREATS

BERRY SMOOTHIE
A real smooth mover who's all glass and
knows how to blend into a crowd.
♥ s helping smooth out problems.

HOMEWARES

COMFY CHAIR

An easy chair to get along
with and always comfortable
to be around.

♥s being a big softy.

TAMMY TV

Wide-eyed and excited, always loud –
until someone turns down her volume.

♥s being the centre of attention.

ACCESSORIES

GARDEN

HANDBAG HARRIET

A little cutie who can handle anything.
Loves to get carried away!

♥s carrying on with her friends.

PETA PLANT

A real head for gardening.
She has a hair-do that's
blooming marvellous!

♥s lazing in the sun!

PARTY TIME

JUNE BALLOON

Never flat and always the life of the party.
So happy she could burst!

♥s decorating.

MISS PRESSY

With the gift of the gab, this generous Shopkin
is the gift that just keeps giving.

♥s party invites and keeping wishes secret.

PETSHOP

GOLDIE FISH BOWL

A really busy bowl who sometimes finds it
hard to keep her head above the water.

♥s deep sea diving.

PRETTY PUFF

Always on the go, she's super
fit and never gets puffed out.

❤ s spreading her sweet scent.

PRETTY BOW KAY

This little cutie looks as pretty
as she smells.

❤ s spraying the day away.

FRENCHY PERFUME

Oh La La! A true romantic who always
dreams of living in Paris.

❤ s sharing breakfast with Croissant d'Or.

SPARKLY SPRITZ

A glamorous Shopkin with
a sparkly personality.

❤ s filling the air with pretty scents.

GEMMA BOTTLE

A cut above the rest! She
always shines when she steps
out on the town.

❤ s the sweet smell of success.

SALLY SCENT

A real sweetheart of a perfume
who can be a little self-scented.

❤ s playing match maker!

MILK BUD

A real moosic lover who never cries when she spills herself.

♥ s making moosic!

BONE-ADETTE

A funny bone who's always yappy, except when she's buried by her doggy friends!

♥ s visiting the butcher shop.

EGGCHIC

A house for a real high flyer and the best nest in town.

♥ s his 'home tweet home'!

RITA REMOTE

A little short-tempered so don't press her buttons!

♥ s changing her tune.

JADE SPADE

A Shopkin who really digs gardening. It's dirty job but someone has to do it!

♥ s spending hours in the garden.

HOT CHOC

Warm and welcoming, she's a great friend to finish off the night with.

♥ s camping.

SHY PIE/CHERRY PIE

Cherry nice and ready to slice, this is a Shopkin you can always 'crust'.

♥ s being a cutie pie.

FISH FLAKE JAKE

Gets a bit shaky when he's around gold fish but is always happy to share at dinnertime.

♥ s sharing his talents.

DRIPS

Can be silly and very spilly! Fill him with water and watch him grow.

♥ s to help in the garden.

JINGLE PURSE

Only has a few coins to her name, but is rich with friends.

♥ s being a real mover and shaker.

ARE YOU A SHOPKINS SUPER-FAN?

How well do you know your fave Shopkins? Try this quiz to find out!

1 Which of these characters is not a Shopkin?
a. Swiss Miss
b. Petra Porridge
c. Lennie Lime

2 Which character belongs in the Health & Beauty aisle?
a. Scrubs
b. Sizzles
c. Peachy

3 Which aisle does Dippy Avocado belong in?
a. Fruit & Veg
b. Pantry
c. Sweet Treats

4 What's the name of the butter Shopkin?
a. Barry Butter
b. Butterfly
c. Buttercup

5 Which Shopkin should not be in the Party Food aisle?
a. Wishes
b. Cheezey B
c. Berry Smoothie

6 Which character belongs in the Sweet Treats aisle?
a. Papa Tomato
b. Snow Crush
c. Candy Kisses

ANSWERS ON PAGE 93

7 Which of these characters is not a Petkin?
a. Jade Spade
b. Tina Treats
c. Hot Choc

8 What colours does Milk Bud come in?
a. Pink and blue
b. Purple and blue
c. Pink and white

9 Which aisle does Kelly Jelly belong in?
a. Sweet Treats
b. Bakery
c. Shoes

10 What's the name of the jam Shopkin?
a. Gran Jam
b. Jerry Jam
c. Sugar Lump

11 Which character belongs in the Petshop aisle?
a. Goldie Fish Bowl
b. Googy
c. Miss Mushy Moo

12 Which character belongs in the Bakery aisle?
a. Silky
b. Patty Cake
c. Chloe Flower

13 What's the name of the bagel Shopkin?
a. Bagel Brenda
b. Billy Bagel
c. Bagel Billy

14 Which aisle does Taylor Rayne belong in?
a. Hats
b. Shoes
c. Homewares

15 What's the name of the watering can Petkin?
a. Molly Mops
b. Chatter
c. Drips

16 Which character is a Season 4 Limited Edition?
a. Ruby Earring
b. Roxie Ring
c. Sally Scent

NOW CHECK YOUR ANSWERS THEN TURN OVER THE PAGE TO FIND OUT YOUR RESULTS!

QUIZ RESULTS!

0-6

SHOPKINS STARTER

You have a bag-full of Shopkins swotting to do before you can be a real super-fan. Try reading back through the 'Meet the Shopkins' pages in this book. You'll be an expert of the aisles in no time!

7-11

COOL COLLECTOR

You're definitely a regular visitor to Shopville with all those correct answers – but you have a few more things to tick off your shopping list. Spend some more time with the Shopkins and who knows what's in store!

12-16

SHOPKINS SUPER-FAN!

Decorate the aisles and make an announcement in store – you're a Shopkins expert! Bet you have a trolley-load of your favourite characters lining the shelves.
Keep it up, you've got the ultimate shopping style.

YOU'RE ALL WINNERS – LIKE ME!

CHECK YA LATER!

It's been SO much fun meeting up with you in Shopville, playing with the Shopkins and hanging with the super-cute Shoppies. Did you meet anyone new? Who's now top of your list to collect or to try and meet at a Shopkins Swapkins club meeting?

How completely adorable are the Petkins? Milk Bud is too cute for words and Jingle Purse is soooo purr-fect. Which one is your favourite? Watch out for Rita Remote – that little cutie could be trouble if you push her buttons!

Make your shopping list for creating the ultimate Shopville at home. Grab your shopping bag and swing by the store to browse your awesome collection.

REMEMBER, ONCE YOU SHOP, YOU CAN'T STOP!

ANSWERS

PAGE 23

There are 11 Shopkins.

PAGES 8-9

Blind Bag: 1. April Apricot,
2. Cheeky Cherries, 3. Peachy,
4. Dippy Avocado, 5. Posh Pear,
6. Apple Blossom.

Mystery Shopkin: Juicy Orange.

Shopkins Shadows: 1. Taco Terrie,
2. Sneaky Sally, 3. Taylor Rayne,
4. Penny Purse, 5. Blushy Brush
6. Roxy Ring.

Aisle Be Quick:

FRUIT & VEG   DAIRY   HEALTH & BEAUTY

PAGE 18

**Fruit & Veg: Posh Pear, Miss
Mushy Moo, Corny Cob, Silly
Chilli, April Apricot; Party Food:
Soda Pops, Wishes, Rainbow
Bite; Bakery: Patty Cake, Toastie
Bread, Bagel Billy, Mini Muffin.**

**The Shopkin that doesn't belong
is Fasta Pasta.**

PAGE 22

PAGE 29

The missing Shopkins are:
Corny Cob, Mini Muffin,
Tommy Ketchup, Mindy Mirror
and Snow Crush.

PAGE 30

Real: 1, 3, 5, 6; Fake: 2, 4, 7, 8.

PAGE 31

1. Chatter, 2. Al Foil,
3. Macca Roon, 4. Leafy

J	A	T	R	O	L	L	E	Y	B
T	S	Z	A	L	F	O	I	L	A
I	U	I	S	V	I	M	P	L	G
L	T	P	A	N	T	R	Y	E	C
L	S	T	O	C	K	V	V	A	H
B	A	K	E	R	Y	Q	Q	F	A
R	A	I	B	N	K	Z	Q	Y	T
M	A	C	C	A	R	O	O	N	T
C	H	E	C	K	O	U	T	Y	E
D	A	I	R	Y	U	W	V	Q	R

PAGES 32-33

**Petkin match: Donatina: Daisy
Donut, Rolly Donut; Jessicake:
Cherry Cake, Coco Cupcake;
Popette: Bowl-inda Popcorn,
Polly Popcorn; Bubbleisha:
Bubblicious, Gumball Gabby;
Peppa-Mint: Icy-Bowl,
Carla Cone.**

Girls' day out:

Photobomb!: 1. Handbag Harriet,
2. Sippy Sips, 3. Prommy,
4. Lolli Poppins, 5. Fairy Crumbs.

PAGE 34

PAGE 35

1. Miss Pressy, 2. Wobbles,
3. Sparkly Spritz, 4. Pretz-elle,
5. Bun Bun Slipper, 6. Honeeey,
7. June Balloon.

PAGES 54-55

PAGES 56-57

Homeware Repair: 1. Vicky Vac,
2. Frost T Fridge, 3. Toasty Pop,
4. Brenda Blender.

Baby Names: 1. Baby Puff,
2. Nappy Dee, 3. Dribbles,
4. Sippy Sips, 5. Baby Swipes.

Small Mart Checkout:
1. c, 2. a, 3. b.

Eggchic for Real:
4 is the real Eggchic.

PAGE 58

Scrubs doesn't have a match.

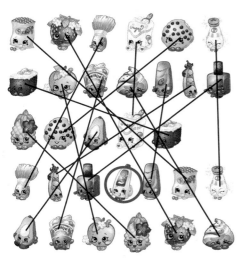

PAGE 67

PAGE 70

1. HOT CHO(C)HEEKY CHERRIES,
2. PANCAKE JAK(E)GGCHIC,
3. CUPCAKE CHI(C)OMFY CHAIR,
4. FIFI FRUIT TAR(T)ACO TERRI,
5. DRIBBLE(S)IZZLES,
6. JENNIFER RAYN(E)RICA ERASER,
7. ROXY RIN(G)RAN JAM,
8. ICE CREAM DREA(M)ILLIE
MINTIE.

PAGE 71

Shampy passes 10 coins

PAGES 72-73

Ready to shop!

1. Popette, 2. Donatina,
3. Jessicake, 4. Bubbleisha.

Peppa-mint's shadow is missing.

Jessicake is ready for
a shopping trip.

PAGE 75

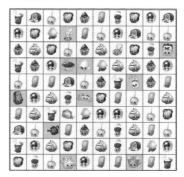

PAGES 82-83

Rub it out: PENNY PENCIL

Sneaky games: HIDE AND SNEAK

Shopkins swapkins:

PAGES 88-89

1. b, 2. a, 3. a, 4. c, 5. c, 6. c, 7. b,
8. a, 9. c, 10. a, 11. a, 12. b, 13. c,
14. a, 15. c, 16. c

SHOPKINS: ANNUAL 2017

A CENTUM BOOK 9781910917213

Published in Great Britain by Centum Books Ltd

This edition published 2016

1 3 5 7 9 10 8 6 4 2

Centum Books Ltd, 20 Devon Square, Newton Abbot, Devon TQ12 2HR, UK

books@centumbooksltd.co.uk

CENTUM BOOKS Limited Reg. No. 07641486

A CIP catalogue record for this book is available from the British Library

Printed in Italy